THE OPEN UN[...]
A SCIENCE FOUNDA[...]

D0480832

UNIT 30 QUANTUM MECHANICS: AN INTRODUCTION

THE SCIENCE FOUNDATION COURSE TEAM

Steve Best (Illustrator)
Geoff Brown (Earth Sciences)
Jim Burge (BBC)
Neil Chalmers (Biology)
Bob Cordell (Biology, General Editor)
Pauline Corfield (Assessment Group and
　　Summer School Group)
Debbie Crouch (Designer)
Dee Edwards (Earth Sciences; S101 Evaluation)
Graham Farmelo (Chairman)
John Greenwood (Librarian)
Mike Gunton (BBC)
Charles Harding (Chemistry)
Robin Harding (Biology)
Nigel Harris (Earth Sciences, General Editor)
Linda Hodgkinson (Course Coordinator)
David Jackson (BBC)
David Johnson (Chemistry, General Editor)
Tony Jolly (BBC, Series Producer)
Ken Kirby (BBC)
Perry Morley (Editor)
Peter Morrod (Chemistry)
Pam Owen (Illustrator)
Rissa de la Paz (BBC)
Julia Powell (Editor)
David Roberts (Chemistry)
David Robinson (Biology)
Shelagh Ross (Physics, General Editor)
Dick Sharp (Editor)

Ted Smith (BBC)
Margaret Swithenby (Editor)
Nick Watson (BBC)
Dave Williams (Earth Sciences)
Geoff Yarwood (Earth Sciences)

Consultants:
Keith Hodgkinson (Physics)
Judith Metcalfe (Biology)
Pat Murphy (Biology)
Irene Ridge (Biology)
Jonathan Silvertown (Biology)

External assessor: F. J. Vine FRS

Others whose S101 contribution has been of
considerable value in the preparation of S102:

Stuart Freake (Physics)
Anna Furth (Biology)
Stephen Hurry (Biology)
Jane Nelson (Chemistry)
Mike Pentz (Chairman and General Editor, S101)
Milo Shott (Physics)
Russell Stannard (Physics)
Steve Swithenby (Physics)
Peggy Varley (Biology)
Kiki Warr (Chemistry)
Chris Wilson (Earth Sciences)

The cover picture is a photograph of a high-energy collision in a bubble chamber, in which a proton with energy 300 GeV collides with a stationary proton. After the interaction many charged particles (mostly pi mesons) are produced. Photo courtesy of Fermi National Accelerator Laboratory.

The Open University, Walton Hall, Milton Keynes, MK7 6AA.

First Published 1988, Reprinted 1989, 1990.

Copyright © 1988, 1989. The Open University.

Designed by the Graphic Design Group of the Open University.

Filmset by Santype International Limited, Salisbury, Wiltshire; printed by Thomson Litho, East Kilbride, Scotland.

ISBN 0 335 16341 6

This text forms part of an Open University Course. For general availability of supporting material referred to in this text please write to: Open University Educational Enterprises Limited, 12 Cofferidge Close, Stony Stratford, Milton Keynes, MK11 1BY, Great Britain.

Further information on Open University Courses may be obtained from the Admissions Office, The Open University, P.O. Box 48, Walton Hall, Milton Keynes, MK7 6AB.

1.3

STUDY GUIDE

This Unit consists of three components—the text, an AV sequence and a TV programme. There are fewer pages than in most other Units, and you should find that your study time is somewhat shorter. However, this Unit contains several subtle concepts that normally each take some time to be absorbed. We should also like to point out that the Unit contains some historical background to the development of quantum physics—you do not have to remember *any* of this historical material.

You should work through the AV sequence 'Wavefunctions of matter' (Tape 5, Side 1, Band 1), which concerns quantum mechanical waves, when you reach Section 3.2 of the text. The sequence should take you about 40 minutes to study.

The TV programme, 'Quantum physics—electrons and photons', can be watched with profit at any stage in your studies of the Unit. Notes for the programme are included in Section 2.

I INTRODUCTION TO THE MODERN PHYSICS BLOCK (UNITS 30–32)

Common sense is something that almost everyone thinks they have in abundance. Although it is a difficult (or perhaps impossible) concept to define, common sense is something that we are often urged to use and to trust.

We have frequently appealed to *your* common sense when we have presented scientific arguments, for example by prefacing apparently uncontentious statements with 'obviously' or 'clearly'. You may have found this irritating, but you would surely agree that *these* two statements are obviously true:

1 When someone walks through a doorway without touching the door frame (Figure 1a), the width of the doorway does not affect the walker's subsequent path.

2 When a stone is dropped down a well (Figure 1b), it is possible to predict for certain where the stone will strike the bottom of the well.

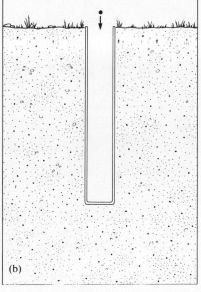

FIGURE 1 Two situations that appear to be amenable to commonsense analyses: (a) someone walking through a doorway; (b) a stone falling down a well.

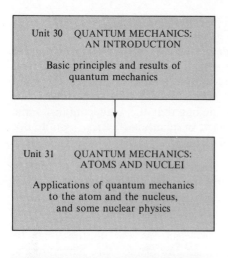

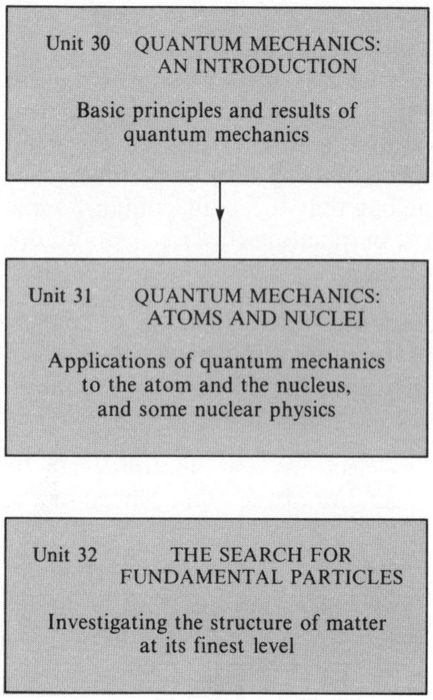

Unit 30   QUANTUM MECHANICS: AN INTRODUCTION

Basic principles and results of quantum mechanics

Unit 31   QUANTUM MECHANICS: ATOMS AND NUCLEI

Applications of quantum mechanics to the atom and the nucleus, and some nuclear physics

Unit 32   THE SEARCH FOR FUNDAMENTAL PARTICLES

Investigating the structure of matter at its finest level

FIGURE 2   The modern physics Block of the Course.

These are uncontentious statements, are they not? Maybe—but they are both believed to be wrong. The theory that implies that the statements are not correct is quantum mechanics, a theory that revolutionized our understanding of the behaviour of matter when it was formulated in the mid-1920s. Until then, motion was believed to be described adequately by the theory of mechanics proposed by Newton almost 250 years before, in 1687 (Unit 3). Newton's laws had given an extremely successful description of matter—the laws could be applied equally well to objects in the everyday world (such as an apple falling from a tree) and to celestial objects (such as the Moon orbiting the Earth). However, soon after the beginning of the 20th century, it was found experimentally that these laws could not account satisfactorily for the behaviour of small-scale matter, such as atoms and subatomic particles. Quantum mechanics does allow this behaviour to be understood, and it can explain how large-scale matter behaves, so this theory has superseded Newtonian mechanics as the best available theory of matter.

This Unit, the first in the modern physics Block (Figure 2), is concerned with some of the most basic concepts and principles of quantum mechanics. It begins by revising the models that are needed to understand the behaviour of electromagnetic radiation (e.g. light), and then goes on to consider the behaviour of matter (electrons, protons, neutrons, etc.). You will see that, contrary to expectations based on everyday experience, each sample of matter has an associated wave. The quantum mechanical interpretation of this wave causes us to abandon the simple commonsense picture of electrons, protons and neutrons, etc., as particles with perfectly defined positions and velocities. According to quantum mechanics, a much more subtle visualization of such microscopic matter is required.

We then move on to discuss one of the most crucial principles of quantum mechanics—the Heisenberg uncertainty principle. This principle radically changed the physicist's view of the concept of measurement. For example, according to Heisenberg, the accuracy with which the *position* of an electron is known unavoidably restricts the accuracy with which its *momentum* can be known simultaneously (and vice versa). This is incomprehensible in terms of Newtonian ideas.

Finally, some of the basic concepts of quantum mechanics are applied to matter in the everyday world in order to see how certain predictions of the theory differ from those based on common sense. When you have completed the Unit, you will have seen that the behaviour of matter is more complicated than it appears to be in everyday life, and you will be able to understand why the two statements made at the beginning of this Introduction are incorrect.

In the remaining two Units in the Block, quantum ideas will be used to probe deeply into the nature and behaviour of matter. You saw earlier in the Course that electrons in atoms have energy levels, that is, they have certain definite values of energy (Figure 3). This is in contrast with everyday experience, according to which the energy of an object is perceived to be a continuously variable quantity (i.e. *not* quantized). Why do electrons in atoms have energy levels? In Unit 31, quantum mechanics will be used to give a straightforward answer to this question, which cannot possibly be answered using Newtonian mechanics. You will also see in Unit 31 that quantum mechanics predicts correctly that atomic *nuclei* also have energy levels, which are generally much more widely spaced in energy than those of atomic electrons. The Unit will also be concerned with some other aspects of the behaviour and properties of nuclei. In particular, radioactive decays will be discussed and we shall explain briefly, in biological terms, why the products of radioactive processes can be hazardous. Also, nuclear fusion and fission will be considered and this will lead us to a brief discussion of nuclear energy.

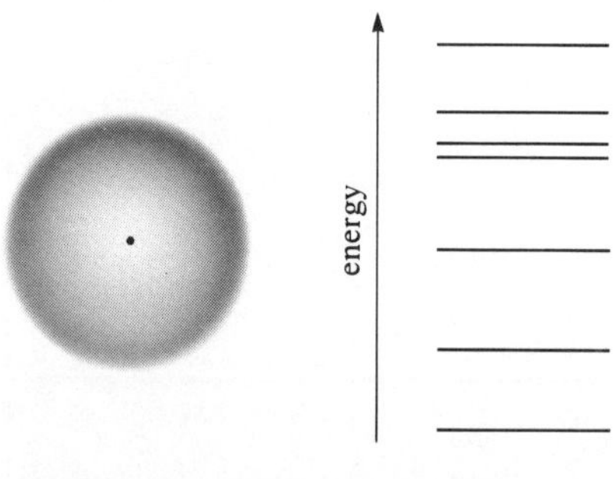

In Unit 32 we shall discuss particle physics, the branch of physics that concerns the behaviour and interactions of subatomic particles, such as electrons, protons and neutrons. You will see that the structure of matter

energy

FIGURE 3   Electrons in atoms have energy levels, i.e. discrete values of energy.

(a)

(b)

FIGURE 4 (a) The outline of the underground super proton synchroton (SPS) at Geneva. (b) The tunnel of the SPS when under construction. (Photos courtesy CERN/Science Photo Library)

can be probed at extremely small distances (typically less than 10^{-15} m, a thousand-million-millionth of a metre) using accelerators that produce beams of particles travelling at speeds extremely close to that of light in a vacuum (Figure 4). In order to understand the behaviour of matter that travels at these speeds, it is essential to use the special theory of relativity. The details of this theory will not be considered in this Block, but in Units 31 and 32 some simple results that follow from the theory will be used. In discussions of matter in Unit 30, only matter that is travelling at speeds much less than that of light in a vacuum will be considered, so relativistic complications will not arise.

The results of experiments done with particle accelerators have shown that the most fundamental description of the structure of matter should be given not in terms of atoms and molecules, but in terms of types of fundamental particle known as leptons, quarks and gauge bosons. As you will see in Unit 32, the behaviour of some of these particles transcends everyday experience: some fundamental particles have unusual properties such as 'strangeness' and 'charm'; some can transform spontaneously into other particles; some are detected only indirectly and are expected *never* to be directly observed!

As you can see, we shall be covering some extraordinary material in this Block. When you have finished the three Units, you may well be quite reluctant to use your common sense when you are analysing scientific problems. You may even agree with Albert Einstein, who once said that 'common sense is the deposit of prejudice laid down in the mind before the age of eighteen'.

2 DESCRIBING THE BEHAVIOUR OF ELECTROMAGNETIC RADIATION AND MATTER (TV PROGRAMME)

In this Section, we shall consider the behaviour of electromagnetic radiation and of matter. First, the two models of electromagnetic radiation that you met in Unit 10 are revised, then models of matter (electrons, protons, neutrons, etc.) are examined. The material in this Section constitutes the broadcast notes for the TV programme 'Quantum physics—electrons and photons'.

2.1 MODELS OF ELECTROMAGNETIC RADIATION

As you saw in Unit 10, light that can be seen by human beings is a particular type of electromagnetic radiation ('radiation' for short) that has wavelengths between approximately 400 nm and approximately 700 nm (remember that $1\,\text{nm} = 10^{-9}\,\text{m}$). There are other types of radiation (for example, γ-rays, X-rays, and microwaves) and each one has a characteristic range of wavelengths (Figure 5). Two entirely different models are required to understand the behaviour of electromagnetic radiation: a wave model, which describes the radiation's propagation, and a particle model, which describes its interactions.

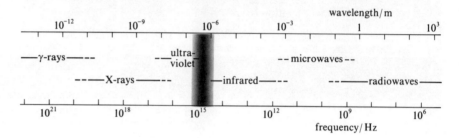

FIGURE 5 The electromagnetic spectrum (note that the boundaries between different regions are not well defined).

2.1.1 WAVE MODEL OF ELECTROMAGNETIC RADIATION

The wave model of radiation is used almost continuously in the analysis of the physics experiment at Summer School. You may remember that in the experiment, a collimated beam of light from a discharge tube propagates towards a diffraction grating, and the diffracted light is observed using an adjustable telescope (Figure 6).

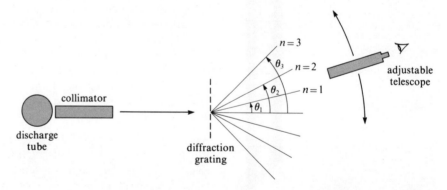

FIGURE 6 When light of wavelength λ impinges on a grating with spacing d, the light is diffracted and the maxima occur at angles θ_n, where $n\lambda = d \sin \theta_n$. This apparatus is used in the physics experiment at Summer School.

For radiation of wavelength λ propagating towards a diffraction grating of spacing d, the angle θ_n of the nth diffracted beam is given by

$$n\lambda = d \sin \theta_n \tag{1}$$

an expression that was derived in Unit 10 using a wave model. For the $n = 1$ beam, Equation 1 says that

$$\lambda = d \sin \theta_1, \quad \text{i.e. } \sin \theta_1 = \frac{\lambda}{d}$$

and for the $n = 2$ beam, Equation 1 says that

$$2\lambda = d \sin \theta_2, \quad \text{i.e. } \sin \theta_2 = 2\left(\frac{\lambda}{d}\right)$$

It is important to remember that diffraction effects are most easily observed (i.e. θ_1 is most easily measurable) if the grating spacing d is not much larger than the wavelength λ of the radiation (Figure 7). If the wavelength is much less than the grating spacing, the diffraction angle θ_1 will be negligibly small—the radiation will appear to propagate straight through (Figure 8).

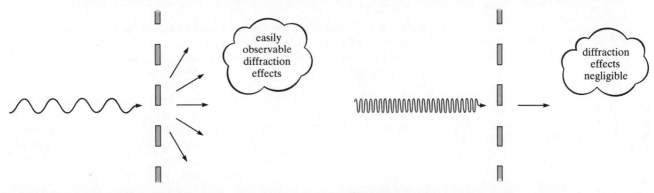

FIGURE 7   Diffraction effects are easily observable if the wavelength of the incident radiation is not much less than the grating spacing.

FIGURE 8   If the wavelength is much less than the spacing, diffraction effects will be negligible.

ITQ 1   A beam of red light with wavelength 700 nm (7.00×10^{-7} m) impinges on a diffraction grating with a spacing of 1 400 nm (1.40×10^{-6} m). Then, in a separate experiment, a beam with the same wavelength is made to impinge on another grating, with a spacing of 1 mm (1.00×10^{-3} m).

(a) In which of the two experiments will diffraction be most clearly evident? (Try to answer this without doing any calculations.)

(b) Calculate the value of θ_1, the angle of the $n = 1$ diffraction maximum, for each experiment. Check that your answer to this part of the question is consistent with your answer to part (a).

You may remember from Unit 10 that, according to the wave model of electromagnetic radiation, a beam of this radiation is associated with an electromagnetic wave. The frequency f of the electromagnetic wave (in a vacuum) is related to its wavelength λ by the relation

$$f = c/\lambda \tag{2}$$

where c is the speed of light (and of any other type of electromagnetic radiation) in a vacuum, approximately $3.00 \times 10^8 \, \text{m s}^{-1}$.

2.1.2 PARTICLE MODEL OF ELECTROMAGNETIC RADIATION

When electromagnetic radiation interacts (i.e. exchanges energy) with matter, its behaviour can be described adequately only in terms of a particle model. According to this model, a beam of electromagnetic radiation is considered as a stream of quanta that each have energy and momentum. Each quantum is called a **photon**.

For a beam of radiation with frequency f, each photon has the same energy E given by the Planck–Einstein formula

$$E = hf \tag{3}$$

where h is Planck's constant, the value of which is approximately 6.63×10^{-34} J s. Note that it is easy to state Equation 3 in an alternative form using the expression for the frequency f given in Equation 2:

$$E = \frac{hc}{\lambda} \tag{4}$$

ITQ 2   Consider again the beam of red light of wavelength 700 nm (7.00×10^{-7} m) described in ITQ 1. What is the energy of each photon in this beam of radiation? (Calculate the answer to two significant figures.)

In Unit 10, you met two types of interaction between radiation and matter—the photoelectric effect and the Compton effect. In the **photoelectric effect**, first explained by Einstein (Figure 9), radiation interacts with matter

FIGURE 9   Albert Einstein (1879–1955) is widely regarded as the most outstanding scientist of the twentieth century. In January 1919, when he and his first wife divorced, he promised that he would give her the money he would receive when his Nobel Prize was awarded. He was as good as his word: four years later, after he won the 1921 Nobel Prize for physics, he gave her the entire 121 572 Kronor (about $32 000). He was awarded the Prize for his 'services to theoretical physics, and especially for his discovery of the law of the photoelectric effect'.

COMPTON EFFECT

in such a way that *all of the energy of an incident photon is transferred to a single electron.* If the amount of energy transferred to the electron is greater than the minimum energy required to remove it from the matter, it will be ejected (Figure 10).

FIGURE 10   In the photoelectric effect, an electron is ejected from a solid after it has absorbed all the energy of an incident photon.

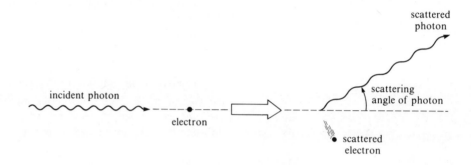

In the **Compton effect**, radiation is *scattered* by an electron—in this case, *not all of the photon's energy is transferred to the electron.* The effect is illustrated in Figure 11: the incoming photon collides with an electron, which thereby acquires kinetic energy. The photon's energy is therefore reduced.

FIGURE 11   In the Compton effect, an electron is scattered by a photon.

☐ Is the wavelength of the scattered radiation shorter than, longer than or the same as that of the incident radiation?

■ Longer. Because the energy of the scattered photon is *lower* than that of the incident photon, the wavelength of the scattered radiation must be *higher* than that of the incident radiation. (Remember from Equation 4 that the energy E of a photon is inversely proportional to the wavelength λ of the radiation.)

In the TV programme, we show how the Compton effect can be studied experimentally, using the apparatus illustrated schematically in Figure 12.

FIGURE 12   A diagram of the apparatus used to demonstrate the Compton effect in the TV programme 'Quantum physics—electrons and photons'.

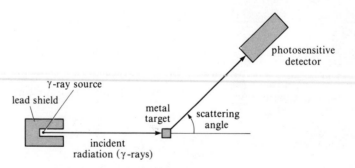

A collimated beam of γ-rays propagates towards a metal target, and the scattered radiation is detected using a photosensitive detector. The photons are scattered at all angles between zero degrees (the 'straight-through' position, which corresponds to no scattering) and 180°, which is the scattering angle of photons that are reflected directly back in their tracks. At each angle, the scattered photons are found to have a characteristic energy and, moreover, the larger the scattering angle, the lower the energy of the scattered photons that are detected at that angle (Figure 13).

The data can be understood only by assuming that each photon has momentum. As you saw in Unit 10, the momentum of a photon has a direction that is the same as that in which the radiation propagates, and the

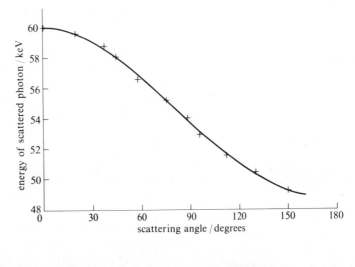

FIGURE 13 In the Compton effect, the greater the scattering angle of the incident photon (Figure 12), the more energy it loses. The data in this Figure refer to the experiment demonstrated in the TV programme 'Quantum physics—electrons and photons'.

magnitude p of the photon's momentum is given by

$$p = E/c \qquad\qquad (5)$$

where E is its energy (remember $E = hf$, Equation 3) and where c is the speed of light in a vacuum. If Equation 5 is used in conjunction with the laws of conservation of energy and momentum, the dependence of a photon's energy loss on its scattering angle can be derived theoretically (we shall not show here how this is done). The theory accounts beautifully for all data on the effect (e.g. Figure 13).

As you saw in Unit 10, the validity of the particle model of light was established by experiments on the Compton effect. These experiments were done by Arthur Compton (Figure 14), who had also been one of the first to formulate a theory of the effect.

SAQ I In Table 1, the photoelectric effect is compared with the Compton effect. Fill in the four gaps in the Table.

TABLE 1 Comparison between the photoelectric effect and the Compton effect (SAQ 1)

	Photoelectric effect	Compton effect
type of process: absorption or scattering?	*absorption*	*scattering*
proportion of the incident photon's energy transferred to the electron	*total*	not all of the photon's energy is transferred
law(s) required to understand the process	conservation of energy	*conservation energy & momentum*

FIGURE 14 Arthur Compton (1892–1962) was awarded a Nobel Prize for physics in 1927 for 'his discovery of the effect named after him'. He did most of this work at the physics department of Washington University in St Louis, Missouri.

2.2 MODELS OF MATTER

You have just seen that the behaviour of electromagnetic radiation can be described in terms of two models—a wave model, which describes the radiation's propagation, and a particle model, which describes its interactions. But what about the behaviour of *matter*, for example the electron? Surely, a particle model is all that is needed to describe its behaviour?

Remember that in this Unit, we shall consider only matter that is travelling at speeds much less than the speed of light in a vacuum. In this way, the complications of the theory of relativity are avoided.

electron

'invariable mass
and charge'

FIGURE 15 According to J. J. Thomson, an electron is a 'small corpuscle with invariable mass and charge'.

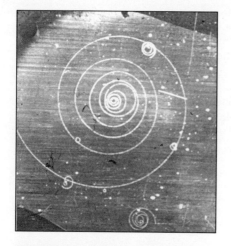

FIGURE 16 The track left by an electron in the liquid hydrogen in a bubble chamber. The track is curved because there is a magnetic field perpendicular to the electron's direction of motion.

2.2.1 PARTICLE MODEL OF MATTER

As you saw in Units 11–12, the English physicist J. J. Thomson discovered the electron in 1897, and for this discovery he was awarded the 1906 Nobel Prize for physics. In his acceptance speech, which he entitled 'Carriers of negative electricity', he referred to electrons as 'particles' and as 'corpuscles, small bodies with an invariable mass and charge' (Figure 15). His ideas received strong support from experiments and by 1916 it had been established that the mass of the electron is approximately 9.1×10^{-31} kg and that its electrical charge is approximately -1.6×10^{-19} C.

It is shown in the TV programme that the path of an electron can be observed using a **bubble chamber**. This device contains a liquid (normally hydrogen) under high pressure. If an electron is propelled into the liquid just as it is about to boil, the electron can ionize the atoms it collides with, leaving in its wake a stream of tiny bubbles that can be illuminated and photographed to show the path of the electron (Figure 16). The leaving of a clearly defined track is, of course, just the behaviour you should expect if the electron were a particle, as Thomson envisaged.

The evidence that supports the idea that the electron is a particle is derived from experiments on its *interactions*: for example, its tracks in liquid hydrogen are observable because it interacts with hydrogen atoms. Experiments on other types of matter (e.g. the proton) confirm that their interactions can be understood only if a particle model is used.

So much for the interactions of matter. Let's now move on to discuss the propagation of matter—the motion of matter when it *does not* exchange energy with other matter.

2.2.2 DE BROGLIE'S WAVE MODEL OF MATTER

In September 1923, Prince Louis de Broglie, a young graduate student at the Sorbonne, came up with a truly extraordinary idea. He suggested that the phenomenon of the wave–particle duality might apply not only to radiation—it might also be exhibited by matter. Perhaps, de Broglie proposed, although matter behaves as a particle when it interacts (i.e. exchanges energy with other matter or radiation), it might behave as a *wave* when it propagates (i.e. when it moves without exchanging energy).

Just over a year later, he submitted his doctoral thesis 'Recherches sur la Théorie des Quanta', which contained the details of his theory. The key idea that he presented was that *every sample of matter has an associated wave*. (This wave is *not* an electromagnetic wave—we shall discuss its nature in the AV sequence.) For a particle that is not subject to a net force, that is a **free particle**, he predicted that the wavelength λ_{dB} of the associated wave is given by Planck's constant h divided by the magnitude p of the particle's momentum:

$$\lambda_{dB} = \frac{h}{p} \qquad (6)$$

This is known as **de Broglie's formula**. It was de Broglie's innovation to apply this relationship to matter, but the expression also applies to radiation, as you will see in ITQ 3.

ITQ 3 Using Equations 2 ($c = f\lambda$), 3 ($E = hf$) and 5 ($p = E/c$), show that for a photon with momentum of magnitude p the quantity h/p is equal to the wavelength λ of the radiation.

For matter (as opposed to radiation), the magnitude p of its momentum is given by the product of its mass m and its speed v

$$p = mv \qquad (7)$$

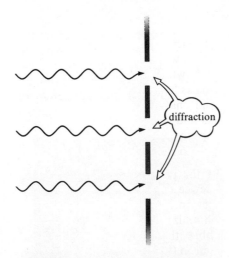

FIGURE 17 Diffraction of matter should be observable if the wavelength of the matter is not much less than the spacing of the grating. (Compare this with Figures 7 and 8.)

as you saw in Unit 3. Substitution of Equation 7 into de Broglie's formula shows that

$$\lambda_{dB} = \frac{h}{mv} \tag{8}$$

Hence, according to de Broglie, for a free mass m, the faster it is travelling (i.e. the higher its speed v), the shorter is its associated wavelength (i.e. the lower is its value of λ_{dB}).

The committee that examined de Broglie's thesis praised the originality of his work and duly awarded him a doctorate, but it appears that the examiners did not believe in the physical reality of the newly proposed waves. Other physicists also received the idea with considerable scepticism and, in some cases, derision. In the absence of data to support what was, after all, only a theoretical conjecture, the idea could be ridiculed with impunity. Louis de Broglie was regarded by many as an eccentric and by some as a crank, but he was taken seriously by Einstein, who stressed the importance of doing experiments to investigate the validity of de Broglie's idea.

How could the idea be checked experimentally? In order to answer this question, think again about the propagation of electromagnetic radiation.

☐ Which type of experiment involving radiation shows that its propagation can be understood only by using a *wave* model?

■ Diffraction experiments. In these experiments, radiation propagates towards a grating whose spacing is not much greater than the wavelength of the radiation (Figure 17).

If each sample of free matter does have an associated wave, then such matter should be noticeably diffracted by a grating with a spacing that is of roughly the same order of magnitude as the matter's wavelength (de Broglie actually pointed this out to the examiners of his thesis!). Consider, for example, a free electron that has been accelerated by a few hundred volts; such an electron has a de Broglie wavelength of approximately 10^{-10} m. Gratings that should noticeably diffract this electron are available in the form of pure metallic crystals which, as you saw in Units 13–14, can be visualized as a regular array of ions in a pool of electrons (Figure 18). Such a structure is closely analogous to that of a conventional optical grating, whose opaque and transparent parts correspond respectively to the ions and the electrons. The average spacing between the ions is, loosely speaking, the 'grating spacing' of the crystal.

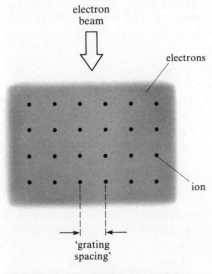

FIGURE 18 A metallic crystal may be regarded as a diffraction grating—the spacing of the ions in the crystal is, loosely speaking, the 'grating spacing'. This illustration shows only a 'slice' through the crystal, which is of course actually three-dimensional.

The question of whether electrons can be diffracted by metallic crystals was investigated in 1925 by Clinton Davisson and his junior collaborator Lester Germer at the Bell Telephone Laboratories in New York. In 1928, G. P. Thomson (the son of J. J. Thomson) independently investigated the question at the University of Aberdeen. The apparatus used by Thomson was similar to the one shown schematically in Figure 19: electrons are accelerated through several hundred volts, propagate through a target of metal foil and are then detected.

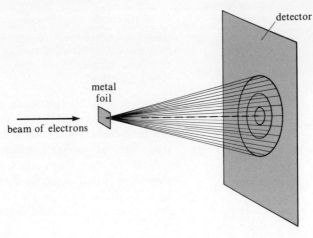

FIGURE 19 Schematic diagram of the type of apparatus used by G. P. Thomson when he observed the diffraction of electrons.

WAVE–PARTICLE DUALITY

QUANTUM

QUANTUM MECHANICS

It was found that the electrons were indeed diffracted and that the observed diffraction patterns were perfectly consistent with expectations based on the de Broglie formula $\lambda_{dB} = h/p$ (e.g. Figure 20a). Moreover, these patterns resemble closely the ones obtained using similar apparatus that used, instead of electrons, a beam of X-rays, i.e. electromagnetic radiation (Figure 20b). This illustrates clearly that diffraction of matter and diffraction of radiation are precisely analogous phenomena.

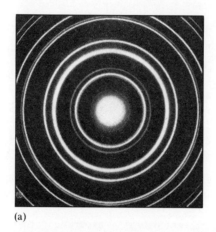 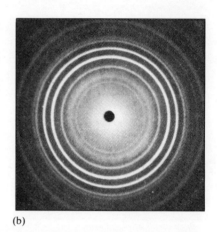

(a)   (b)

FIGURE 20   (a) A diffraction pattern obtained using a beam of electrons and a target of gold crystals, in the configuration shown in Figure 19. (b) A diffraction pattern obtained using a beam of X-rays and a target of zirconium oxide crystals, also in the configuration shown in Figure 19.

Thus, de Broglie's revolutionary idea that a wave is associated with each sample of free matter was vindicated, at least for electrons (it was later checked that the idea applied equally well to other types of matter, e.g. protons, neutrons, nuclei, atoms and molecules). The conclusion was inescapable: the idea of **wave–particle duality** applies both to electromagnetic radiation *and* matter.

Louis de Broglie (Figure 21) was subsequently awarded the 1929 Nobel Prize for physics and, eight years later, the Prize was shared by Davisson and G. P. Thomson. The Thomson family certainly did make diverse contributions to our understanding of the electron. G. P. Thomson's Nobel Prize was awarded for his verification of the *wave* model of the electron, whereas his father, J. J. Thomson, had received his Prize for demonstrating that the electron behaves as a *particle*!

FIGURE 21   Prince Louis de Broglie (1892–1987) was of noble descent, his ancestors having served French monarchs since the time of Louis XIV. He was awarded the 1929 Nobel Prize for physics for 'his discovery of the wave nature of electrons'.

2.3 QUANTA AND QUANTUM MECHANICS

You have now seen that there is an analogy between the behaviour of electromagnetic radiation and that of matter. A particle model is required to describe their interactions, whereas a wave model is needed to describe their propagation. Hence, there is a problem of terminology: it is not strictly correct to describe matter (electrons, protons, neutrons, etc.) and electromagnetic radiation simply as 'particles' or as 'waves'. These terms each apply only in certain circumstances ('particles' for their interactions, 'waves' for their propagation).

It is therefore convenient to apply the term **quantum** to radiation *and* matter—by definition, a quantum behaves as a particle in interactions and as a wave in propagation. The advantage of using this term is that it avoids the need separately to specify whether propagation or an interaction is being described.

Although it is best to refer to electrons, protons, neutrons, etc., as quanta, it must be admitted that the use of the term to describe matter is somewhat unconventional. Scientists nearly always refer to electrons, protons, neutrons, etc., as particles, which of course should strictly speaking be used only to describe them when they interact. In the remaining Units of the Course, we shall normally follow this widely accepted convention, and we hope that you will tolerate this laxity. However, in this Unit we shall continue to use the 'quantum' terminology.

You may already have wondered whether there exists a theory that can describe both the propagation *and* interactions (i.e. wave and particle behaviour) of matter, just as the theory of quantum electrodynamics can describe the propagation and interaction of radiation (Unit 10). Such a theory has been formulated—it is called **quantum mechanics**. Sometimes the term *quantum theory* is used as a synonym for quantum mechanics, but we shall use the former term in a more general sense to encompass all the theoretical concepts that apply to all quanta (i.e. matter *and* radiation).

In the remainder of this Unit, some of the basic concepts of quantum mechanics will be described and then, in Unit 31, they will be applied to the atom and the nucleus.

SUMMARY OF SECTION 2

1   The propagation of electromagnetic radiation is described by a wave model, which enables the diffraction of radiation to be understood.

2   The interactions of electromagnetic radiation with matter can be described by a particle model in which each quantum of radiation (photon) has an energy $E = hf$ and a momentum of magnitude $p = E/c$, in the usual notation. This model enables the photoelectric effect and the Compton effect to be understood.

3   The propagation of free matter is described by de Broglie's wave model, according to which free matter has an associated wavelength $\lambda_{dB} = h/p$, in the usual notation. This model successfully predicted that electrons can be diffracted.

4   The interactions of matter can be understood using a particle model.

5   The idea of wave–particle duality applies to both electromagnetic radiation and matter.

6   Quantum mechanics is a theory that describes the wave and particle behaviour of matter.

SAQ 2   (a) A student doing the physics experiment at Summer School arranges for a collimated beam of sodium light with a wavelength of 589 nm to impinge perpendicularly on a diffraction grating whose spacing is 1 670 nm. At what angle will the $n = 1$ diffraction maximum be observed?

(b) At what angle would the $n = 1$ diffraction maximum have occurred if the student had used, instead of light, a collimated beam of free electrons with a speed of $1.00 \times 10^6 \, \mathrm{m\,s^{-1}}$? (Take the mass of the electron as $9.11 \times 10^{-31} \, \mathrm{kg}$, and remember that $1 \, \mathrm{J} = 1 \, \mathrm{kg\,m^2\,s^{-2}}$.)

SAQ 3   A beam of X-rays has a frequency of 10^{18} Hz. (Remember that $1 \, \mathrm{Hz} = 1 \, \mathrm{s^{-1}}$).

(a) What is the energy of each X-ray photon?

(b) What is the momentum of each X-ray photon?

SAQ 4   Fill in the two missing bits of evidence in Table 2 (*overleaf*).

SAQ 5   Which *two* of the following statements about quantum mechanics are correct?

(a) It can describe the propagation of visible light.

(b) It can describe the interactions of electrons.

(c) It can describe the propagation of electrons.

(d) It applies only to electrons.

13

TABLE 2 Summary of experimental evidence for the particle and wave models of electrons and electromagnetic radiation (SAQ 4)

Model	Experimental evidence
particle model of the electron	☐ the electron has a definite charge and mass
	☐ an electron can leave a clearly defined track in a bubble chamber
wave model of the electron	☐ *diffraction by ionic substance*
particle model of electromagnetic radiation	☐ photoelectric effect
	☐ *Compton effect*
wave model of electromagnetic radiation	☐ diffraction (e.g. the physics experiment at Summer School)

3 QUANTUM MECHANICAL DESCRIPTIONS OF MATTER

In this Section, the extraordinary nature of the type of wave associated with matter will be described. Then, in the AV sequence 'Wavefunctions of matter', the waves associated with matter in different circumstances (free and confined) will be illustrated and discussed.

3.1 WHAT TYPE OF WAVE IS ASSOCIATED WITH MATTER?

Consider the experiment shown schematically in Figure 22: a beam of free electrons (i.e. matter) impinges on a single slit and a diffraction pattern is observed on a screen, which serves as a detector. This is precisely analogous to the observation that light is diffracted when it is shone on a single slit (Unit 10).

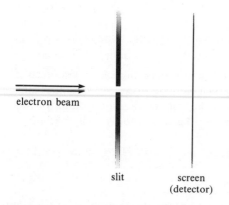

FIGURE 22   A beam of electrons impinges on a single slit. Diffracted electrons are subsequently detected on a screen.

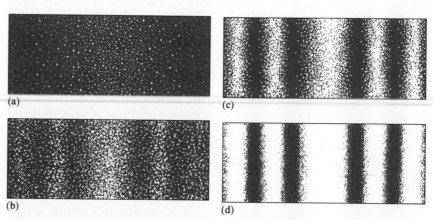

FIGURE 23   As more electrons arrive at the screen (Figure 22), a diffraction pattern gradually builds up.

Each electron is observed to arrive at a definite point on the screen, and, as more electrons are detected, the diffraction pattern builds up. When only a few electrons have arrived, a pattern is scarcely observable (Figure 23a), but it gradually becomes easier to discern (Figures 23b–d) until eventually a practically smooth distribution is observed. This distribution can be represented conveniently by a graph of the intensity of the pattern plotted against diffraction angle (Figure 24). The intensity in a given small region represents the number of electrons that are detected in that region in a given time.

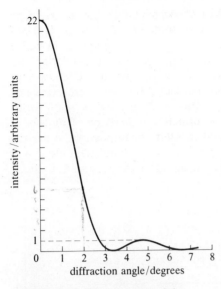

FIGURE 24 The intensity of the diffraction pattern plotted against diffraction angle (relative to the straight-through position).

In Figure 24, you can see that the number of electrons that arrive at a small area around the straight-through position (zero diffraction angle) is approximately 22 times the number that arrive at a small area around the first diffraction maximum (where the diffraction angle is approximately 4.8°). Notice that *no* electrons are detected at the diffraction *minima*.

The observation that each individual electron arrives at a definite point somewhere on the screen can be understood using a *particle* model. However, the shape of the diffraction pattern can be predicted successfully only by using de Broglie's *wave* model, according to which the positions of the diffraction maxima should depend only on the wavelength of the beam (remember, $\lambda_{dB} = h/p$) and on the width of the slit.

So far so good; you will probably not have been surprised by this description of electron diffraction. But let us now consider more closely the behaviour of an individual electron in the beam. Is it possible to predict where the electron will *not* be detected? The answer is Yes—the wave model of electrons can be used to predict the positions of the diffraction minima, where no electrons arrive.

Now another question: is it possible to predict for certain where an individual electron *will* be detected? Believe it or not, the answer is No—*it is absolutely impossible to predict for certain where a particular electron will be detected*. It is possible to predict only the relative probability that the electron will arrive in a particular region of the detector. For example, in the case depicted in Figure 24, the electron is approximately 22 times as likely to be detected in an area opposite the slit (zero diffraction angle) as it is to be detected in an area of the same size around the first diffraction maximum (a diffraction angle of about 4.8°).

ITQ 4 How much more likely is an electron to be detected in a small area around the straight-through position (zero diffraction angle) than it is to be detected in an area of the same size around the diffraction angle of 2°?

Just as it is not possible to predict for certain where the electron will be detected, so it would be impossible to predict where any other type of matter would be detected after it had been diffracted by the slit.

Hence, a physicist who is asked to predict the behaviour of a single quantum of matter is in rather a similar position to that of opinion pollsters before an election. The pollsters can forecast with reasonable accuracy the percentage of an electorate that will vote for each party, but they cannot predict with certainty the party for which a randomly selected individual will vote (without actually asking!).

All this talk of being able to predict only the odds on the outcome of the diffraction of a single quantum may well strike you as very strange. Isn't physics an exact science? Let us try to anticipate your objections to this unpredictability: consider the following argument put forward by a sceptic.

> The nature of the diffraction experiment you have described has not been specified carefully enough. All you have said is that an electron passes *somewhere* through the slit. If an extremely careful study were made of the incident electron, its original path could be determined precisely and this determination would enable you to identify the atom (or atoms) in the rim of slit with which the electron interacts. It should then be possible to calculate (in principle, at least) precisely how the electron is scattered from the atom (or atoms), and hence it should be possible to determine the direction in which the scattered electron travels. That would enable you to calculate *exactly* where the electron strikes the detector.

This commonsense argument is based on the crucial assumption that *it is possible to determine precisely where the electron enters the slit and, at the same time, its direction of motion*.

How could this assumption be checked experimentally? Let us begin by trying to specify very accurately the position of the electron as it passes through the slit. We shall use the apparatus shown in Figure 25, in which the electrons emerge from a hole H (in a container) positioned right up against the slit S. If the hole were extremely small, we should know very accurately *where* the electron enters the slit. But if the hole were extremely small, *the electron could be significantly diffracted by the hole before it enters the slit.* Hence, we should not know accurately the *direction* of motion of the electron as it enters the slit. It would therefore be impossible to use the laws of conservation of energy and momentum to work out the outcome of the collision of this electron with any particular atom (or atoms) in the slit.

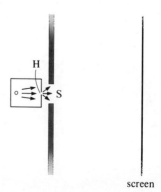

screen

FIGURE 25   A configuration of the apparatus shown in Figure 22: electrons emerge from a tiny hole H that is close to the single slit S.

So much for an attempt to fix accurately the *position* of the electron before it enters the slit. Let us now adopt a different strategy and try to fix its *direction*, using *only* the apparatus shown schematically in Figure 26, in which the slit S is very far away from the hole H. Now, because the slit subtends such a small angle with respect to the centre of the hole H, the direction of motion of the electron as it passes through the slit is defined quite accurately (Figure 26). Unfortunately, because the electron's direction is specified so accurately, our knowledge of the position of the electron as it passes through S has had to be sacrificed. It is not known whether the atom (or atoms) at the rim of the slit is (or are) being struck a glancing blow or a direct hit, or indeed which atom (or atoms) is (or are) being struck. Once again, the laws of conservation of energy and momentum cannot be used to find the path of the electron after it emerges from the slit.

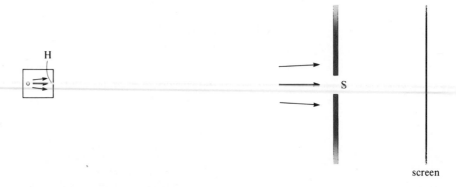

screen

FIGURE 26   Another configuration of the apparatus shown in Figure 22: electrons emerge from a hole H that is very distant from the single slit S.

We hope that you are now convinced that it is *not* possible to predict with certainty where an *individual* electron will be detected after it has been diffracted. It is possible to predict accurately only the diffraction pattern produced by a *very large number* of electrons, and this pattern can be used to calculate the *probabilities* of an individual electron's arrival in different regions of the detector. This conclusion applies equally well to other types of matter, e.g. protons, neutrons, atoms and molecules, when they are diffracted.

Now let us return to the problem of specifying the nature of the wave associated with each sample of matter. You saw in Unit 10 that the wavelength of a light wave and the width of the illuminated slit determine the

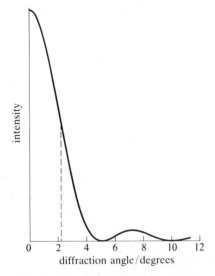

FIGURE 27   See SAQ 6.

optical diffraction pattern. You have now seen that the pattern produced by the diffraction of matter determines the *probabilities* that a quantum of matter will arrive at given regions of the detector. It should therefore be plausible to you that

---

the wave associated with a quantum of matter is in turn associated in some way with the relative probabilities of detecting the quantum in different regions of space.

In Section 3.2, we shall discuss further the nature of the wave associated with each quantum of matter and we shall show how such waves can be visualized.

SAQ 6   A beam of free protons propagates towards a single slit, and a diffraction pattern is detected behind the slit (the apparatus is very similar to the one shown in Figure 22). The intensity of the diffraction pattern that is observed (after many protons have been detected) is shown in Figure 27.

(a) In which region of the screen is an individual proton in the beam *most* likely to be detected?

(b) In which region(s) of the screen will an individual proton definitely *not* be detected?

(c) What is the probability that an individual proton will be observed with a diffraction angle of 2.2° (relative to the probability that it will be observed with zero diffraction angle)?

3.2 WAVEFUNCTIONS (AV SEQUENCE)

You should now study the AV sequence 'Wavefunctions of matter' on Tape 5, Side 1, Band 1, then have a go at SAQs 7–9.

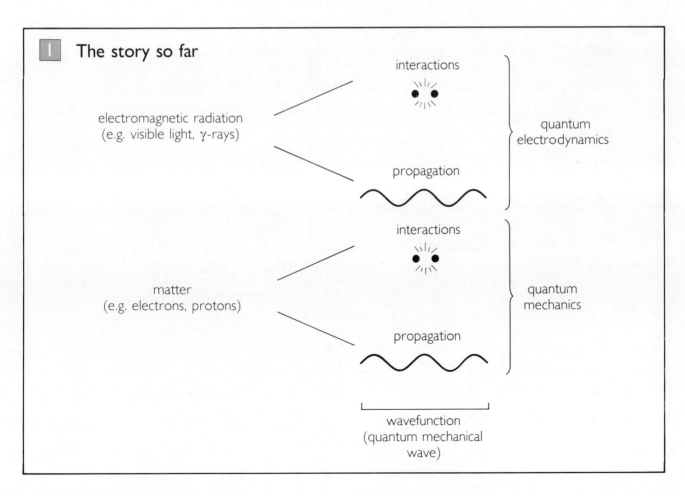

2 Two types of wave on a rope

(i) *Infinite sine waves*

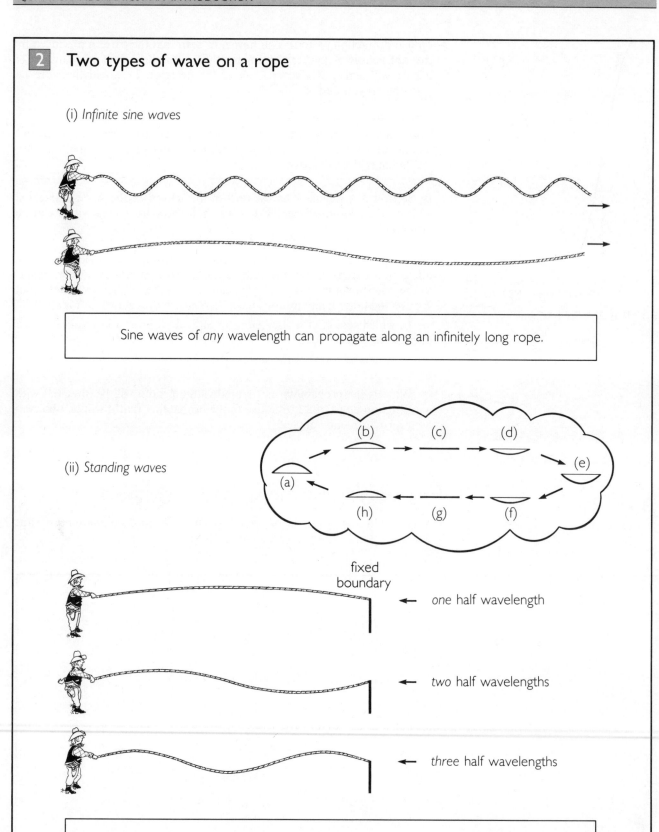

> Sine waves of *any* wavelength can propagate along an infinitely long rope.

(ii) *Standing waves*

fixed
boundary

← *one* half wavelength

← two half wavelengths

← *three* half wavelengths

> Each standing wave has a whole number of half-wavelengths between its fixed ends.

3   Two types of wavefunction

(i) *Infinite sine waves as wavefunctions*

associated with a *free* quantum (i.e. a quantum on which zero net force acts)

(ii) *Standing waves as wavefunctions*

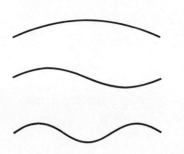

associated with a quantum that is *confined* between two parallel, impenetrable reflecting plates that are infinitely high, separated by distance L

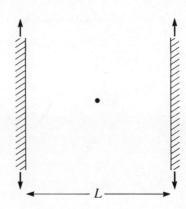

What do these wavefunctions mean?

4   Interpreting wavefunctions

- difficult to discuss rigorously

- we shall consider only the interpretation of wavefunctions that are standing waves

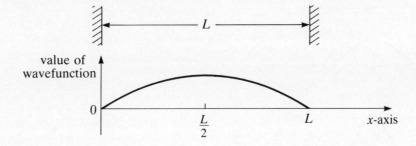

The probability of detecting a quantum of matter in a given small region of space is proportional to the square of the value of the wavefunction in that region.

5 Examples of wavefunctions

Example 1

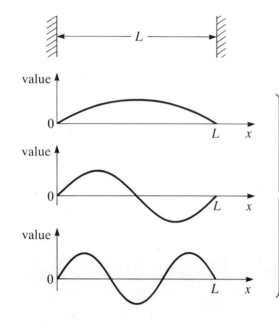

for *every* wavefunction
value outside plates = 0

so

probability of detecting the quantum
outside the plates = 0

Example 2

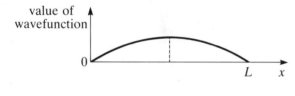

← When the quantum is described by this
wavefunction ...

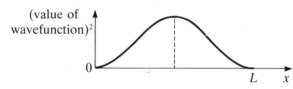

... the quantum is most likely to be detected
mid-way between the plates, because at
this point the square of the value of
wavefunction has its maximum value

Example 3

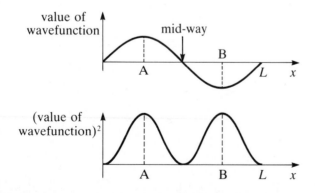

When the quantum is described by *this*
← wavefunction ...

– the quantum will not be detected
mid-way between the plates

– the probability of detecting the quantum
at **A** = the probability of detecting it at **B**

6 Questions

Example 4

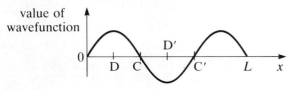

□ What is the probability of detecting the quantum at **C** and at **C**′?

■ ....

□ Is the probability of detecting the quantum at **D** more than, less than or equal to the probability of detecting it at **D**′?

■ ....

> The probability of detecting a quantum in a small region of space depends crucially on the wavefunction that describes the quantum.

7 Infinite sine waves as wavefunctions

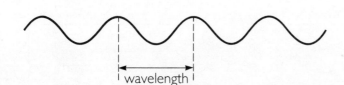

wavelength

associated with a *free* quantum
(i.e. a quantum not subject to a net force)

wavelength given by $\lambda_{dB} = \dfrac{h}{p}$

— Planck's constant

— magnitude of momentum

8   Calculating wavefunctions

☐   How can the possible wavefunctions of a quantum of matter be calculated?

■   Using the Schrödinger equation.

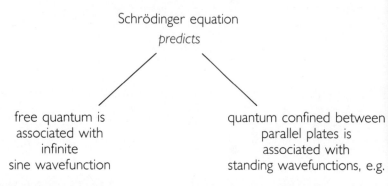

Schrödinger equation
predicts

free quantum is
associated with
infinite
sine wavefunction

quantum confined between
parallel plates is
associated with
standing wavefunctions, e.g.

Erwin Schrödinger
(1887–1961)

9   Summary

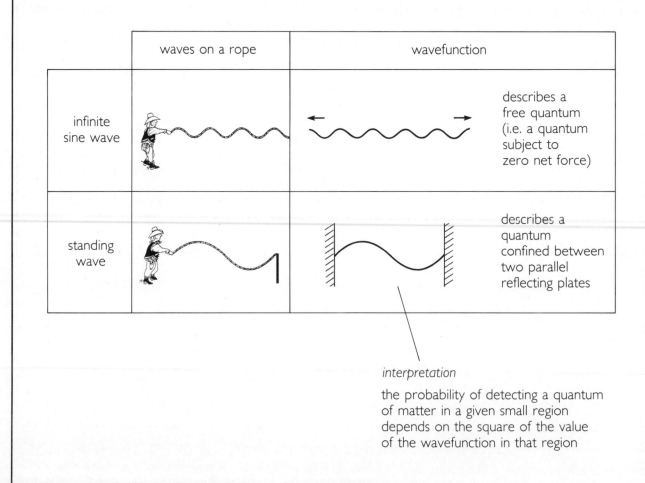

	waves on a rope	wavefunction	
infinite sine wave			describes a free quantum (i.e. a quantum subject to zero net force)
standing wave			describes a quantum confined between two parallel reflecting plates

interpretation

the probability of detecting a quantum
of matter in a given small region
depends on the square of the value
of the wavefunction in that region

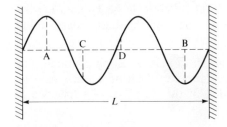

FIGURE 28   See SAQ 9.

SAQ 7   Sketch a wavefunction of (a) a proton that is subject to zero net force; (b) a neutron confined between two infinite, parallel, impenetrable reflecting plates.

SAQ 8   What is the wavelength of the wavefunction of a free electron that has a speed of $2.00 \times 10^6 \, \mathrm{m \, s^{-1}}$?

SAQ 9   Refer to Frame 3 of the AV sequence, which shows a quantum that is confined between two reflecting plates. If the wavefunction of the quantum is the one shown in Figure 28,

(a) What is the probability of detecting the quantum mid-way between the plates?

(b) Is the probability of detecting the quantum at A less than, greater than or equal to the probability of detecting it at B?

(c) Is the probability of detecting the quantum at C less than, greater than or equal to the probability of detecting it at D?

SUMMARY OF SECTION 3

1   The quantum mechanical wave that is associated with a quantum of matter is called a wavefunction.

2   The value of the wavefunction of a quantum of matter in a small region of space determines the probability of detecting the quantum in that region—a comparatively large magnitude of the value corresponds to a comparatively high probability of detection.

3   The wavefunction of a quantum of matter that is confined between two infinite, parallel, impenetrable, reflecting plates is a standing wave.

4   The wavefunction of a free quantum of matter (i.e. a quantum subject to zero net force) is an infinite sine wave.

4 HEISENBERG'S UNCERTAINTY PRINCIPLE

You saw in Section 3.1 that when a quantum is diffracted, its subsequent path cannot be predicted for certain: it is possible to predict only the *probability* that the quantum will be diffracted in a certain angular region. This uncertainty in the quantum's behaviour is a manifestation of Heisenberg's uncertainty principle, which gives fundamental limits to the accuracy with which a quantum's motion can be specified. This principle is one of the cornerstones of quantum mechanics and it cannot possibly be understood in terms of Newtonian ideas (Unit 3).

Our discussion of the principle will begin by considering in detail the motion of matter on the large scale. Then you will see how a simple mathematical form of the principle can be derived by analysing a thought experiment that concerns the diffraction of a beam of electrons by a single slit. Finally, the principle is applied to electrons in atoms.

4.1 SPECIFYING THE MOTION OF MACROSCOPIC OBJECTS

As you will see shortly, in order to discuss the Heisenberg uncertainty principle in detail, we shall need to specify carefully the motion of 'microscopic' matter, such as electrons, protons and neutrons. In order to prepare the ground for this discussion, we must now describe precisely how a descrip-

ONE-DIMENSIONAL MOTION

TWO-DIMENSIONAL MOTION

COMPONENTS OF POSITION

COMPONENTS OF VELOCITY

COMPONENTS OF MOMENTUM

THREE-DIMENSIONAL MOTION

tion of macroscopic (i.e. large-scale) objects is given in Newtonian mechanics. We shall do this by developing some of the basic ideas about mechanics that you first met in Units 3 and 9.

Consider the motion of a large-scale object of mass m along a straight line that can be labelled as the x-axis (Figure 29). This is known as **one-dimensional motion** because the position of the object can be specified at

$t = 0$ $t = 1\,\mathrm{s}$ $t = 2\,\mathrm{s}$ $t = 3\,\mathrm{s}$
$v = 0$ $v = +2\,\mathrm{m\,s^{-1}}$ $v = +1\,\mathrm{m\,s^{-1}}$ $v = -2\,\mathrm{m\,s^{-1}}$

0   0.5   1.0   1.5   2.0
distance x from initial position/m

FIGURE 29   An example of one-dimensional motion. At each time, the position and velocity can each be specified by a single quantity.

each time t in terms of *one* quantity, its position x relative to its *initial* position, which is labelled $x = 0$. The velocity v of the object is represented by a bold arrow whose direction is the same as that of the object's direction of motion and whose length is proportional to the speed of the object. For the example that is illustrated in Figure 29: at $t = 1\,\mathrm{s}$ (one second after the motion began), $x = 0.5\,\mathrm{m}$ and $v = +2\,\mathrm{m\,s^{-1}}$ (to the right); at $t = 2\,\mathrm{s}$, $x = 1.5\,\mathrm{m}$ and $v = +1\,\mathrm{m\,s^{-1}}$ (to the right); and at $t = 3\,\mathrm{s}$, $x = 2\,\mathrm{m}$ and $v = -2\,\mathrm{m\,s^{-1}}$ (to the left). The arrow starting from the point $x = 0.5\,\mathrm{m}$ is twice as long as the arrow starting from $x = 1.5\,\mathrm{m}$ because the speed of the object at the former position is twice its speed at the latter position.

It is convenient to define the momentum p of an object

$$p = mv \qquad\qquad\qquad (7)*$$

You may remember from Unit 3 that momentum is important because it is conserved when a system is not subject to a net force. Moreover, we shall be particularly concerned with this variable when we discuss the uncertainty principle.

How can the concepts of position, velocity and momentum be generalized from the simple case of motion in a straight line to **two-dimensional motion**, in which the object can move *in a plane?*

Consider, for the sake of definiteness, an object of mass $m = 0.5\,\mathrm{kg}$ that moves on the surface of the graph in Figure 30, having begun its motion at time $t = 0\,\mathrm{s}$, stationary at $x = 0\,\mathrm{m}$ and $y = 0\,\mathrm{m}$. This may seem to be a somewhat artificial situation—motion on the surface of a piece of graph paper is hardly the most familiar of phenomena! This situation is undoubtedly artificial, but that is not important—what *is* important is that the graph and its fixed axes enable us conveniently to keep track of the object's two-dimensional motion. Look, for example, at Figures 31a and 31b, which illustrate the positions and velocities of the object at $t = 1\,\mathrm{s}$ and $t = 2\,\mathrm{s}$, respectively.

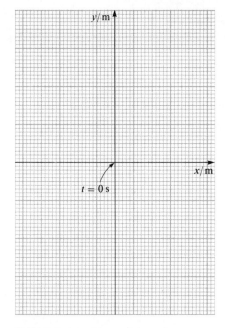

FIGURE 30   The position of a particle moving in two dimensions can be specified by x- and y-coordinates.

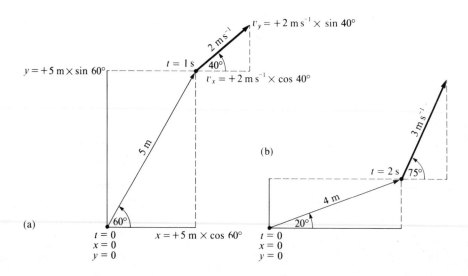

FIGURE 31   Examples of two-dimensional motion at two instants.

At $t = 1\,\text{s}$ (Figure 31a), the object is at a distance of $5\,\text{m}$ from its starting point, at an angle of $60°$ relative to the x-axis. Its position may also be specified in terms of its values of x and y, which are known as **components of position**:

position component x = component of position in the x-direction

position component y = component of position in the y-direction

As you can see from Figure 31a, at $t = 1\,\text{s}$,

$$x = 5\,\text{m} \times \cos 60° = 2.50\,\text{m} \tag{9a}$$

$$y = 5\,\text{m} \times \sin 60° = 4.33\,\text{m} \tag{9b}$$

What about the velocity of the object? The bold arrow on Figure 31a shows that the speed of the object (i.e. the *magnitude* of its velocity) is $2\,\text{m s}^{-1}$ and that the velocity is directed at an angle of $40°$ relative to the x-axis. This is the object's direction of motion at the time—the direction in which it is moving—which should not be confused with the angle ($60°$) that the object position makes with the x-axis.

Just as the object's position can be specified in terms of position components (x and y), its velocity can also be specified in terms of **components of velocity**:

velocity component v_x = component of velocity in the x-direction

velocity component v_y = component of velocity in the y-direction

Figure 31a shows that, at $t = 1\,\text{s}$,

$$v_x = 2\,\text{m s}^{-1} \times \cos 40° = 1.53\,\text{m s}^{-1}$$

$$v_y = 2\,\text{m s}^{-1} \times \sin 40° = 1.29\,\text{m s}^{-1}$$

These velocity components also enable us to calculate the **components of momentum**, p_x and p_y, of the object at $t = 1\,\text{s}$:

$$p_x = mv_x = 0.5\,\text{kg} \times 1.53\,\text{m s}^{-1} = 0.77\,\text{kg m s}^{-1} \tag{10a}$$

$$p_y = mv_y = 0.5\,\text{kg} \times 1.29\,\text{m s}^{-1} = 0.65\,\text{kg m s}^{-1} \tag{10b}$$

ITQ 5 Figure 31b shows the position and velocity of the object (which has mass $0.5\,\text{kg}$) at $t = 2\,\text{s}$. Calculate the following quantities at this time: (a) the object's position components; (b) the object's velocity components; (c) the object's momentum components.

You have now seen that one-dimensional motion (i.e. motion in a straight line) can be specified at a given time in terms of single components of position, velocity and momentum. On the other hand, two-dimensional motion (i.e. motion in a plane) can be specified in terms of pairs of components—of position (x, y), velocity (v_x, v_y) and momentum (p_x, p_y). It should not now surprise you that it is possible to specify **three-dimensional motion** (i.e. motion in *any* direction, Figure 32) in terms of triplets of components—of position (x, y, z), velocity (v_x, v_y, v_z) and momentum (p_x, p_y, p_z).

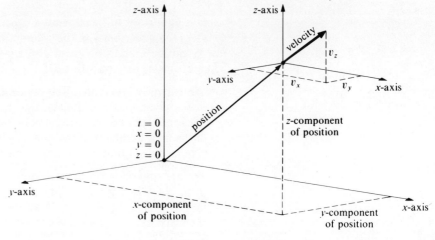

FIGURE 32 The position and velocity of a particle that executes three-dimensional motion can each be specified by three components (x, y, z) and (v_x, v_y, v_z).

25

So far, we have implicity assumed that the position, velocity and momentum of the object can all be specified simultaneously (i.e. at the same time) with perfect accuracy. Our everyday experience suggests that this is a very reasonable assumption: after all, shouldn't we expect that the position and velocity of a macroscopic object, such as a tennis ball, could in principle be specified to arbitrarily high accuracy? Surely it is reasonable to say that, at any given instant, the ball is in a definite place moving with a definite velocity? We shall return to these questions (and re-examine the answers!) in Section 5, but first let's compare this 'commonsense' perception of the behaviour of macroscopic objects in our everyday world with the behaviour of a microscopic quantum, such as an electron.

4.2 SPECIFYING THE MOTION OF A QUANTUM—THE HEISENBERG UNCERTAINTY PRINCIPLE

In order to introduce the Heisenberg uncertainty principle, we shall discuss a thought experiment in which a single slit diffracts a beam of free electrons (the analysis applies equally well to all other quanta). In this experiment, each electron has momentum of magnitude p, and the single slit has width w (Figure 33). Notice that the x- and y-axes on the apparatus illustrated in Figure 33 have been set up in such a way that $x - 0$ and $y - 0$ are in the centre of the slit.

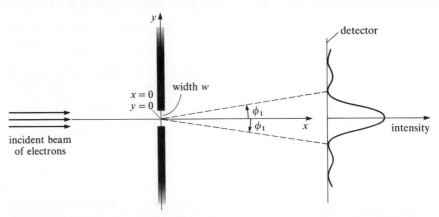

FIGURE 33   When an electron is diffracted by a single slit, it is likely (but not certain) that its angle of diffraction will be less than ϕ_1 (the angular position of the first diffraction minimum).

We shall consider measurements of the position and momentum of electrons in the beam as they pass through the slit, and for definiteness we shall concentrate on the y-components of these quantities. First, think about an experiment to measure the y-component of the positions of the electrons as they pass through the slit. Such an experiment would show that the values of y extend from $+w/2$ to $-w/2$ (Figure 34a). We say that the uncertainty in the y position component of an electron in the beam is $w/2$, and we denote this uncertainty by the symbol Δy:

$$\Delta y = \frac{w}{2} \tag{11}$$

It is important to be clear about the meaning of Δy: although this quantity gives the uncertainty in the y-component of the position of a *single* electron, Δy can be found only from a series of measurements of y taken with *many* electrons as they pass through the slit.

We can now generalize the concept of quantum mechanical uncertainty. For a given experimental set-up, the **uncertainty in a quantum mechanical measurement** of a quantity may be taken to be half the spread of the results of the measurements of the quantity. More rigorously, the uncertainty is the standard deviation of the measurements (Unit 4).

We are now in a position to derive a form of the Heisenberg uncertainty principle. First, we shall find an expression for the uncertainty Δp_y in the momentum component p_y of an electron as it passes through the slit, and then we shall multiply this expression by the uncertainty Δy (Equation 11).

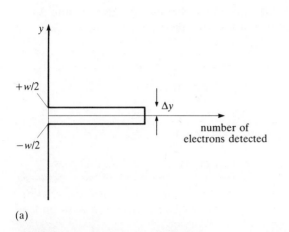

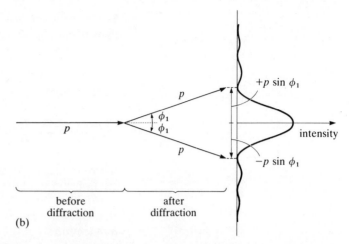

(a)

(b)

FIGURE 34 (a) If, for a number of electrons, the y-component of position is measured, as the electrons pass through a slit of width w, the results will be evenly spread from $y = +w/2$ to $-w/2$. The uncertainty Δy is $w/2$, half the spread w. (b) The y-component p_y of the momentum of the electrons is *likely* to lie between $+p \sin \phi_1$ and $-p \sin \phi_1$ (some values of p_y will lie *outside* this range because the diffraction pattern extends past the diffraction angle ϕ_1).

As you will see shortly, this particular combination of uncertainties gives a very simple result.

In order to find the uncertainty Δp_y in the y-component of the momentum of an electron in the beam, we need to consider where the electrons strike the screen after they have passed through the slit.

☐ At what angle will an electron in the beam be diffracted?

■ It is impossible to say. As you saw in Section 3, it is possible to give only the *probabilities* that the electron will arrive in different small regions of the screen.

Although it is not possible to predict the angle at which an electron in the beam is diffracted, it *is* possible to say that there is a high probability that the electron will be detected somewhere in the central diffraction peak, i.e. that the diffraction angle is likely to be between 0 and ϕ_1, either side of the straight-through position (Figure 33). This implies that measurements of the y-component p_y of momentum *after* diffraction will *probably* be between $+p \sin \phi_1$ and $-p \sin \phi_1$ (Figure 34b). Hence, it is reasonable to assert that the uncertainty Δp_y is approximately $p \sin \phi_1$ (i.e. half the spread):

$$\Delta p_y \approx p \sin \phi_1 \tag{12}$$

The quantity $\sin \phi_1$ is given by

$$\sin \phi_1 = \frac{\lambda_{dB}}{w} \tag{13}$$

where λ_{dB} is the de Broglie wavelength of the free electron. Equation 13 is precisely analogous to the corresponding expression for the diffraction of light by a single slit, which you met in Unit 10. When the expression for $\sin \phi_1$ in Equation 13 is substituted into Equation 12 we find:

$$\Delta p_y \approx p \frac{\lambda_{dB}}{w} \tag{14}$$

In Section 2, the de Broglie wavelength of a free quantum was given as

$$\lambda_{dB} = \frac{h}{p} \tag{6*}$$

When this expression is substituted into Equation 14, we find

$$\Delta p_y \approx \frac{h}{w} \tag{15}$$

The product of Δy and Δp_y is therefore given by

$$\Delta y \times \Delta p_y \approx \frac{w}{2} \times \frac{h}{w} \tag{16}$$

using Equations 11 and 15. Hence,

$$\Delta y \Delta p_y \approx \frac{h}{2} \tag{17}$$

HEISENBERG'S UNCERTAINTY PRINCIPLE

So, according to our analysis, the product of the uncertainties Δy and Δp_y is approximately $h/2$, half the value of Planck's constant.

By using a more rigorous analysis, it can be shown that the product $\Delta y \Delta p_y$ is actually *greater than or equal to* Planck's constant h divided by 4π. In mathematical notation, the correct relationship between Δy and Δp_y is

$$\Delta y \Delta p_y \geqslant \frac{h}{4\pi} \qquad (18a)$$

where the sign $\geqslant$ means 'greater than or equal to', that is, 'at least'. This relationship is quite general—it applies to *all* quanta in *all* circumstances, not only to electrons that are diffracted by a single slit. Also, the relationship applies equally well to the other two components of position and momentum:

$$\Delta x \Delta p_x \geqslant \frac{h}{4\pi} \qquad (18b)$$

$$\Delta z \Delta p_z \geqslant \frac{h}{4\pi} \qquad (18c)$$

Notice that the principle refers to the products of position components and the *corresponding* momentum components—it says nothing about products such as $\Delta x \Delta p_y$, $\Delta z \Delta p_y$ and $\Delta y \Delta p_z$. The relationships in Equations 18a–c are known as *Heisenberg's uncertainty relations* after Werner Heisenberg (Figure 35), who was the first to formulate them, in 1927. The relations embody **Heisenberg's uncertainty principle**, or 'the uncertainty principle' for short.

HEISENBERG'S UNCERTAINTY PRINCIPLE

The product of the uncertainty in a component of the position of a quantum (e.g. Δy) and the uncertainty in the corresponding component of the quantum's momentum at the same time (e.g. Δp_y) is at least $h/4\pi$, e.g.

$$\Delta y \Delta p_y \geqslant \frac{h}{4\pi} \qquad (18a)*$$

The principle also applies to certain other pairs of variables (for example, energy and time) but we shall not be concerned with these other forms of the principle in this Course.

At first sight, the principle may appear only to give technical limitations on the accuracy with which the motion of a quantum can be specified. However, the principle is more important than that—it is of fundamental significance in quantum physics. And, as the following example shows, the principle has some truly remarkable consequences.

Consider a quantum, say a proton, whose *x*-component of position is known with perfect accuracy. What does the uncertainty principle have to say about the *x*-component of momentum of the proton *at the same time?* Well, since the *x*-component of the proton's position is assumed to be known with perfect accuracy, it follows that the uncertainty Δx in the proton's *x*-component of position is zero

$$\Delta x = 0 \qquad (19)$$

The appropriate uncertainty relation, Equation 18b, then implies that

$$\Delta p_x \geqslant \frac{h}{4\pi \Delta x} \qquad (20)$$

so $\quad \Delta p_x = \infty \qquad (21)$

because $h/0 = \infty$, infinity. Hence, there is in this case infinite uncertainty in p_x, which implies that nothing at all is known about the value of p_x. This remarkable result is worth summarizing—if the *x*-component of position of

FIGURE 35 Werner Heisenberg (1901–1976) was awarded the Nobel Prize for physics in 1932 for 'his discovery of the uncertainty principle'. Although he was undoubtedly a great theoretician, it appears that his practical skills left something to be desired. In his PhD oral examination, his responses to questions on experimental physics were so poor that one of his examiners, the Nobel Prize winning physicist Wilhelm Wien, recommended that he should fail! (He was eventually awarded a pass for the exam—grade three.)

a quantum is known with perfect accuracy ($\Delta x = 0$), it follows from the uncertainty principle that nothing at all can be said for certain about the x-component of the quantum's momentum at the same time. (Similar reasoning can be applied to the other pairs of components: e.g. if $\Delta z = 0$, then $\Delta p_z = \infty$.) Hence, if you know exactly where a quantum is, you cannot know both how quickly, and in which direction, it is moving!

ITQ 6 Consider a quantum, say an electron, whose y-component of momentum is known with perfect accuracy. What does the Heisenberg uncertainty principle say about the accuracy with which the y-component of the quantum's position is known at the same time?

You have now seen that the uncertainty principle implies that the accuracy with which a position component of a quantum can be specified depends crucially on the accuracy with which the corresponding momentum component is specified (and vice versa). If one of the quantities is known very accurately, the other must perforce be known very *inaccurately*.

You may well be wondering if this restriction on the accuracies with which position and momentum components can be specified can be overcome by sufficiently ingenious experimental design. In fact, it cannot—the restriction is *fundamental* in the sense that it reflects the behaviour of nature, not a deficiency in the design of measuring apparatus. According to the uncertainty principle, no matter how well the apparatus is designed and constructed, the restriction on the accuracies with which position components and corresponding momentum components can be specified simultaneously *cannot be overcome*.

If you are one of those who find this difficult to accept, don't worry, you have been in good company. Einstein always believed that it should be possible *in principle* to measure position components, momentum components and all other variables of every quantum simultaneously to arbitrarily high accuracy, given sufficiently accurate and well-designed equipment. Heisenberg has described how, at a conference in 1927, Einstein went to considerable trouble to convince his friend and colleague Niels Bohr (one of the great pioneers of quantum physics) that the uncertainty principle is not valid.

> And so he [Einstein] refused point-blank to accept the uncertainty principle, and tried to think up cases in which the principle would not hold.
>
> The discussion usually started at breakfast, with Einstein serving us up with yet another imaginary experiment by which he thought he had definitely refuted the uncertainty principle. We would at once examine his fresh offering, and on the way to the conference hall, to which I generally accompanied Bohr and Einstein, we would clarify some of the points and discuss their relevance. Then, in the course of the day, we would have further discussions on the matter, and, as a rule, by suppertime we would have reached the point where Niels Bohr could prove to Einstein that even his latest experiment failed to shake the uncertainty principle.
>
> (Heisenberg, 1949)

Einstein never did manage to refute the uncertainty principle. Indeed, no one has ever been able to show that it is theoretically or experimentally invalid—Heisenberg's uncertainty principle is now universally accepted and is one of the tools of the trade for the professional quantum mechanic.

4.3 APPLYING THE UNCERTAINTY PRINCIPLE TO ATOMS

You saw in Units 11–12 that each atom consists of electrons moving around a charged nucleus (except the hydrogen atom, which contains only one electron). According to commonsense ideas, electrons in a many-electron atom can each be visualized as having a clearly defined path

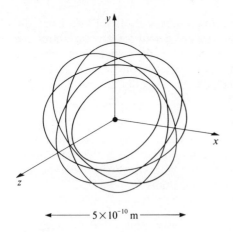

5×10^{-10} m

FIGURE 36 A simple visualization of an atom, according to which each electron has a clearly defined path (A set of x-, y- and z-axes has been set up with the origin at the centre of the nucleus.)

(Figure 36). In such a visualization, it is implicitly assumed that the position and direction of motion of each electron are known with perfect accuracy at the instant at which the illustration applies. However, the uncertainty principle says that such an accurate specification is not possible.

So how accurately *can* the position and momentum of an electron be simultaneously specified? In order to answer this question, we shall consider the uncertainties that would arise in experiments to measure, at a given instant, the position and momentum of an electron in a typical atom, which has a diameter of 5×10^{-10} m. For convenience, we shall draw x-, y- and z-axes in the atom that we are considering, with $x = y = z = 0$ at the centre of the nucleus.

We shall now use the uncertainty principle to show that the confinement of an electron in an atom implies that there is a considerable uncertainty in each component of the electron's velocity. The discussion will concentrate on motion relative to the x-axis, although the arguments apply equally well to motion with respect to the other two axes.

The uncertainty Δx in the x-component of the position of an electron in an atom may reasonably be estimated as being 2.5×10^{-10} m, approximately equal to half the typical diameter of an atom (Figure 36):

$$\Delta x = 2.5 \times 10^{-10} \text{ m} \tag{22}$$

Now that we have an estimate for Δx, the uncertainty principle allows us to find Δp_x, the uncertainty in the corresponding specification of the x-component of the momentum of the electron. Because $\Delta x \Delta p_x \geqslant h/4\pi$ (Equation 18b) it follows that

$$\Delta p_x \geqslant \frac{h}{4\pi \, \Delta x} \tag{20}*$$

i.e. $\quad \Delta p_x \geqslant \dfrac{6.63 \times 10^{-34} \text{ J s}}{4 \times 3.14 \times 2.50 \times 10^{-10} \text{ m}} \tag{23}$

so† $\quad \Delta p_x \geqslant 2.11 \times 10^{-25} \text{ kg m s}^{-1} \tag{24}$

The uncertainty Δp_x in the x-component p_x of the momentum of the electron is related to the uncertainty Δv_x in the x-component v_x of the electron's velocity using Equation 7:

$$\Delta p_x = m_e \, \Delta v_x \tag{25}$$

Note that we are assuming that the *uncertainty* Δm_e in the mass of the electron is negligible.

From Equation 25, the uncertainty Δv_x in the x-component of the electron's velocity is

$$\Delta v_x = \frac{\Delta p_x}{m_e} \tag{26}$$

so, using this equation and the result in Equation 24,

$$\Delta v_x \geqslant \frac{2.11 \times 10^{-25} \text{ kg m s}^{-1}}{9.11 \times 10^{-31} \text{ kg}} \tag{27}$$

i.e. $\quad \Delta v_x \geqslant 2.3 \times 10^5 \text{ m s}^{-1} \tag{28}$

This is a remarkable conclusion: the uncertainty Δv_x in the x-component of velocity of an electron in an atom is at least 230 thousand metres per second! This result has followed directly from the Heisenberg uncertainty principle in conjunction with the reasonable assumption that $\Delta x = 2.5 \times 10^{-10}$ m for an electron in an atom. Because Δy and Δz are also

† The standard SI unit of momentum, kg m s^{-1}, is equivalent to the unit J s m^{-1}: you saw in Unit 9 that $1 \text{ J} = 1 \text{ N m} = 1 \text{ kg m}^2 \text{ s}^{-2}$, so $1 \text{ J s m}^{-1} = 1 \text{ kg m s}^{-1}$.

FIGURE 37 A quantum mechanical visualization of an atom (the electrons are visualized as a fuzzy cloud).

approximately equal to 2.5×10^{-10} m, it follows that Δv_y and Δv_z are greater than or approximately equal to 230 thousand metres per second as well.

The uncertainty principle therefore says that because the electron in an atom is confined to a tiny region of space, it follows that the corresponding *uncertainty in each component of the electron's velocity is more than two hundred thousand metres per second!* This is in sharp contrast with expectations based on Newtonian mechanics, according to which the electron's velocity could in principle be known with *zero* uncertainty! It should now be plain to you that the picture of the atom given in Figure 36 must be radically revised. Somehow, it must be shown that the speed and direction of motion of each confined electron is very uncertain.

The conventional quantum mechanical visualization of an atom is shown in Figure 37. The electrons are shown as a cloud whose fuzziness symbolizes the limits on our knowledge of the position and momentum of each electron at a given time (the same picture is used to visualize a hydrogen atom). Aside, it is worth remarking that the picture of the atom in Figure 37 is consistent with what you learned about quanta of matter in the AV sequence 'Wavefunctions of matter'. An atomic electron is described by a wavefunction that, as you will see in Unit 31, spreads across the whole atom, and this wavefunction gives the probability of detecting the electron in each tiny region of the atom.

The Heisenberg uncertainty principle has one other very important implication—it implies that there is no state of an atom in which a constituent electron will be observed to be permanently at rest. In order to understand why, suppose for a moment that an atomic electron *did* permanently have zero velocity. This would imply that the uncertainty in the electron's momentum components were each zero ($\Delta p_x = \Delta p_y = \Delta p_z = 0$) so, according to the uncertainty principle, there would be *infinite* uncertainty in the electron's position components, $\Delta x = \Delta y = \Delta z = \infty$ (ITQ 6)! This cannot be the case because atomic electrons are normally confined to a *tiny* region of space ($\Delta x = \Delta y = \Delta z = 2.5 \times 10^{-10}$ m). Hence, the initial suggestion—that there exist atomic states in which a constituent electron permanently has zero velocity—cannot be true. For any atomic state, measurements of the electron's velocity will give a range of values with a spread consistent with the uncertainty principle. This is a purely quantum effect, and it cannot possibly be understood within the framework of Newtonian mechanics.

SUMMARY OF SECTION 4

1 According to ideas based on Newtonian mechanics, it is possible to give an accurate description of the motion of a particle (at each instant) by specifying the position and momentum of the particle to arbitrarily high accuracy.

2 According to the Heisenberg uncertainty principle, one of the cornerstones of quantum mechanics, if there is an uncertainty Δx in the instantaneous x-component of the position of a quantum, then the uncertainty Δp_x in the corresponding x-component of the quantum's momentum is constrained by the requirement

$$\Delta x \Delta p_x \geqslant \frac{h}{4\pi} \tag{18b)*}$$

and the same is true for the y- and z-components of position and momentum. These constraints on our knowledge of position and momentum components cannot be overcome by using better experimental apparatus to measure the quantities.

3 The uncertainty principle implies that the electrons in an atom (or the single electron in a hydrogen atom) should be visualized as a fuzzy cloud that symbolizes the uncertainties in the position and momentum of each electron.

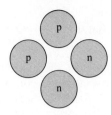

FIGURE 38 A simplistic visualization of a helium nucleus.

SAQ 10 At a party in Islington, you meet an amateur philosopher who tells you that 'according to the Heisenberg uncertainty principle, everything in physics is uncertain'. You are dismayed by the superficiality of this statement and you resolve to correct it. In simple, non-mathematical terms, explain to your fellow guest the true meaning of the uncertainty principle.

SAQ 11 In an elementary textbook on nuclear physics, a helium nucleus (which contains two protons and two neutrons and has a diameter of approximately 10^{-14} m) is visualized as in Figure 38.

(a) What is the uncertainty in each component of the velocity of one of the quanta (a proton or neutron) in the nucleus? (Use the data on the back cover and calculate your answer to two significant figures.)

(b) Use your answer to part (a) to suggest a better way of visualizing the helium nucleus.

SAQ 12 Using the Heisenberg uncertainty principle, explain why there is no state of a nucleus in which a constituent proton or neutron is permanently at rest.

SAQ 13 You saw in the AV sequence that the magnitude of the momentum of a free quantum has a definite value p and that the wavelength of the quantum's wavefunction is given by $\lambda_{dB} = h/p$. In terms of the uncertainty principle, explain qualitatively why the wavefunction of the quantum must be of infinite extent.

5 QUANTUM MECHANICS AND THE LARGE-SCALE WORLD

At the end of Section 4.1, we pointed out that in the everyday world we *assume* that we can specify the position and velocity of objects (such as tennis balls) to an accuracy limited only by our measuring techniques and our equipment. But is the assumption correct, or does quantum mechanics apply to macroscopic objects as well as to microscopic quanta? In this short Section, the answer to this question will be given and one of its consequences will be discussed in detail.

5.1 DOES QUANTUM MECHANICS APPLY TO MACROSCOPIC OBJECTS?

The short answer to this question is Yes: *quantum mechanics is believed to apply to all matter**. This has some profound implications for our understanding of the everyday world.

As you have seen, according to quantum mechanics

(a) each quantum of matter is associated with a wavefunction;

(b) the accuracies with which the quantum's position and momentum components can be simultaneously specified are limited by the Heisenberg uncertainty principle;

(c) the quantum can be diffracted.

Because quantum mechanics is believed to apply equally well to macroscopic objects as to microscopic quanta (electrons, protons, atoms, etc.), it follows that *the above results should also apply to macroscopic objects*.

---

* With the proviso that the matter is not moving with a speed close to that of light in a vacuum, in which case a *relativistic* version of quantum mechanics must be used.

FIGURE 39 Someone walking through a doorway.

You may well be very sceptical of that last statement! Does the uncertainty principle *really* apply in the everyday world? Can a macroscopic object be diffracted? In Section 5.2, the latter question will be considered in detail.

5.2 DIFFRACTION OF MACROSCOPIC OBJECTS

The sight of someone walking through a doorway (Figure 39) is common enough. Nothing appears to happen to the walker on passing through the doorway, and their path is independent of the doorway's width (provided that it is wide enough for the walker to pass through without coming into contact with the door frame). However, quantum mechanics leads us to expect that this situation is not as simple as it first appears to be. The person walking through the doorway has an associated wave and the doorway itself may be regarded as a single slit (Figure 40). Hence, the walker should be diffracted! Yet if this is so, why haven't you ever been conscious of being diffracted when you pass through a doorway?

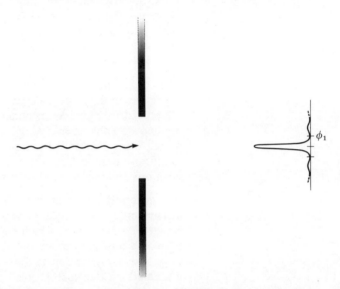

FIGURE 40 The situation shown in Figure 39 can be modelled quantum mechanically as a wave passing through a single slit.

Let us examine the situation more closely. Suppose that the walker is someone with a mass of 50 kg, walking with a speed of $1 \, \text{m s}^{-1}$ through a doorway of width 0.80 m. In order to estimate the maximum probable angle of diffraction, we shall assume that the walker can be regarded as a free particle. The de Broglie formula can then be used to calculate their wavelength.

ITQ 7 What is the walker's de Broglie wavelength λ_{dB}?

You saw in ITQ 7 that the walker's de Broglie wavelength λ_{dB} is very much smaller than the width of the doorway. Hence, you should expect immediately that they will not be significantly diffracted; diffraction will be significant only if the wavelength is not much smaller than the width of the slit.

☐ Is it possible to predict precisely the angle at which the walker will be diffracted?

■ No, but it is possible to predict the probabilities with which the walker will be diffracted in a given angular region. Also, it is likely that the walker will be diffracted by an angle that is less than ϕ_1, the angle at which the first diffraction minimum occurs (Figure 40). This macroscopic situation is exactly analogous to the microscopic example illustrated in Figure 33.

The angle ϕ_1 may be estimated using Equation 13

$$\sin \phi_1 = \frac{\lambda_{dB}}{w} \tag{13}*$$

where w is the width of the doorway. Because $\lambda_{dB} = 1.3 \times 10^{-35}\,\text{m}$ (ITQ 7) and $w = 0.80\,\text{m}$, Equation 13 implies that

$$\sin \phi_1 = \frac{1.3 \times 10^{-35}\,\text{m}}{0.80\,\text{m}}$$

$$\sin \phi_1 = 1.6 \times 10^{-35}$$

i.e. $\phi_1 \sim 10^{-33}$ degree

Hence, the walker would be diffracted by an angle of no more than about 10^{-33} degree, i.e. a thousand-million-million-million-million-millionth of a degree! This is such a small angle that the diffraction could not possibly be observed.

This simple calculation illustrates an important general result: *quantum mechanics predicts that although macroscopic objects are diffracted, the angles at which such objects are diffracted are negligible*. The diffraction of macroscopic objects can generally be neglected because of the smallness of their de Broglie wavelengths.

Just as the diffraction of matter is observable on the microscopic scale but negligible on the large scale, so most other quantum mechanical results that are crucial in allowing an understanding of electrons, protons, atoms, etc., are unobservable in everyday life. For example, the Heisenberg uncertainty principle can be applied to macroscopic objects but the results do not give significant practical limitations to the accuracies with which the objects' positions and momenta may be specified.

It is generally true that in the everyday world the predictions of quantum mechanics agree almost perfectly with the corresponding predictions of Newtonian mechanics, which describes extremely well the motion of macro-scopic objects, as you saw in Unit 3. There are, however, many macroscopi-cally observed phenomena that can be explained only by applying quantum mechanics to the microscopic constituents of matter. A classic example of this is the phenomenon of superconductivity, in which the resistance to electric current of some substances falls to zero below a critical temperature (each of these substances has a characteristic value of this temperature). Superconductivity was discovered in 1911 by the Dutch physicist Kamer-lingh Onnes, but it was not until 1957 that the phenomenon was explained quantum mechanically by the American physicists John Bardeen, Leon Cooper and John Schrieffer.

You should leave this Section in no doubt that quantum mechanics is superior to Newtonian mechanics as a theory of matter. Whereas Newton's theory can be relied upon to account successfully for the motion only of large-scale objects, quantum mechanics describes the behaviour of all matter—microscopic and macroscopic.

SUMMARY OF SECTION 5

1   Quantum mechanics applies to all matter, microscopic quanta (e.g. elec-trons, atoms and molecules) and macroscopic objects. Hence, quantum mechanics is superior to Newtonian mechanics, which accounts successfully only for the motion of macroscopic objects.

2   Quantum mechanics predicts that macroscopic objects can be diffracted, but diffraction effects for such objects are far too small to be observable.

3   The motion of macroscopic objects can be predicted using quantum mechanics, but these predictions differ negligibly from those of Newtonian mechanics.

SAQ 14 Which of the following situations do you expect to be successfully accounted for (i) by quantum mechanics and (ii) by Newtonian mechanics?

(a) The motion of a neutron in a uranium nucleus;

(b) The behaviour of a carbon atom in a carbon dioxide molecule;

(c) The motion of a football across Wembley stadium;

(d) An apple falling from a tree.

SAQ 15 At the beginning of this text, we said that the statements below are strictly speaking false, although they appear (according to common sense) to be true. Explain briefly why each statement is wrong according to quantum mechanics.

1 When someone walks through a doorway without touching the door frame, the width of the doorway does not affect the walker's subsequent path.

2 When a stone is dropped down a well, it is possible to predict for certain where the stone will strike the bottom of the well.

6 EPILOGUE TO UNIT 30

In this Unit, you have seen how quantum ideas have revolutionized our view of matter. We began with a revision of the wave and particle models of electromagnetic radiation. Both models are incorporated in quantum electrodynamics. The propagation and interactions of *matter* can also be understood fully only if both wave *and* particle models are used. Quantum mechanics allows the propagation and interactions of matter to be understood within the framework of a single theory, a theory of the *behaviour* of matter. Quantum mechanics does not deal with a sample of matter simply as a particle or as a wave, rather it deals with matter as a particle when it interacts and as a wave when it propagates.

We have not shown how the theory of quantum mechanics is formulated—that would have been beyond the scope and level of this Course—but we have discussed some of the theory's principal results and we have described how they are interpreted.

The quantum mechanical ideas that you have met were proposed in the 1920s, nearly 250 years after Newton formulated his theory of mechanics. Newton could not have developed quantum mechanics because neither he nor his contemporaries had apparatus that could motivate the need for such a theory or check its predictions. However, that is not to belittle Newton's work, which was triumphantly successful by any standards. It gave many profound insights to the scientists who developed quantum ideas—clearly, if quantum mechanics was to be a worthy successor to Newtonian mechanics, it was essential for the new theory to reproduce the success of its predecessor in accounting for the behaviour of macroscopic objects. In Section 5, you saw that quantum mechanics was indeed successful in this way—it could be applied to matter in the large-scale world, although quantum effects are far too small to be observed for macroscopic objects.

This implied that a number of conventional ideas about the behaviour of matter must be abandoned. For example, quantum mechanics says that

When you walk through a doorway, you are diffracted;

When you are diffracted, your angle of diffraction cannot be predicted exactly, even in principle;

If you know exactly where you are, you cannot possibly know both your speed and the direction in which you are moving.

Do you still trust your common sense?

OBJECTIVES FOR UNIT 30

After you have worked through this Unit, you should be able to

1 Explain the meaning of, and use correctly, all the terms flagged in the text.

2 Recall evidence for the wave and particle models of matter. (*SAQs 1 and 4*)

3 Recall the de Broglie formula $\lambda_{dB} = h/p$ and apply it to simple problems of physics. (*ITQ 3 and 7; SAQs 2 and 8*)

4 Recall the range of applicability of quantum mechanics. (*SAQs 5, 14 and 15*)

5 Interpret the diffraction pattern observed when matter is diffracted. (*ITQ 4 and SAQ 6*)

6 Sketch the wavefunctions of matter that is (a) free, (b) confined between parallel plates; also, interpret the wavefunctions in the latter case. (*AV; SAQs 7 and 9*)

7 Calculate the position, velocity and momentum components of a macroscopic object that moves in one or two dimensions (*ITQ 5*)

8 State the Heisenberg uncertainty principle and apply it to simple physical situations, e.g. electrons in atoms, protons and neutrons in nuclei. (*ITQ 6, SAQs 10–13*)

9 Apply simple quantum mechanical ideas to macroscopic objects (*ITQ 7, SAQs 14 and 15*).

ITQ ANSWERS AND COMMENTS

ITQ 1 (a) Diffraction effects will be more clearly evident in the experiment with the grating whose spacing is 1 400 nm: diffraction effects are significant only if the grating spacing is not much larger than the wavelength of the incident radiation. (Note that 1 mm, i.e. 10^{-3} m, is much greater than 700 nm, 7×10^{-7} m.)

(b) For the grating with a spacing of 1 400 nm, $\theta_1 = 30°$; for the grating with a spacing of 10^{-3} m, $\theta_1 = 0.040°$.

Using Equation 1, $n\lambda = d \sin \theta_n$, with $n = 1$

$$\sin \theta_1 = \frac{\lambda}{d}$$

Hence, when $\lambda = 700$ nm and $d = 1\,400$ nm

$$\sin \theta_1 = \frac{700 \text{ nm}}{1\,400 \text{ nm}} = 0.5, \quad \text{i.e. } \theta_1 = 30°$$

and when $d = 1$ mm,

$$\sin \theta_1 = \frac{7.00 \times 10^{-7} \text{ m}}{1.00 \times 10^{-3} \text{ m}} = 7.00 \times 10^{-4},$$

i.e. $\theta_1 = 0.040°$.

This is consistent with the answer to part (a): diffraction effects are more clearly evident (i.e. θ_1 is greater) in the experiment with the grating whose spacing is 1 400 nm.

ITQ 2 The energy of each photon in the beam is 2.8×10^{-19} J. Using Equation 4, the energy E of each photon is

$$E = \frac{(6.63 \times 10^{-34} \text{ J s}) \times (3.00 \times 10^8 \text{ m s}^{-1})}{7.00 \times 10^{-7} \text{ m}}$$

i.e. $E = 2.8 \times 10^{-19}$ J

ITQ 3 Using Equation 5 ($p = E/c$ for a photon),

$$\frac{h}{p} = \frac{hc}{E}$$

Because $E - hf$ for a photon (Equation 3), it follows that

$$\frac{hc}{E} = \frac{hc}{hf} = \frac{c}{f}$$

Equation 2 tells us that $c/f = \lambda$, so h/p (the quantity with which we began) is equal to the wavelength λ of the radiation. In other words, for electromagnetic radiation, the de Broglie wavelength λ_{dB} is equal to the ordinary wavelength λ of the radiation.

ITQ 4 About 3.7 times more likely, because the intensity in the straight-through position is approximately 3.7 times the intensity at a diffraction angle of 2°. The intensity in the straight-through position is approximately 22 units, and the intensity when the diffraction angle is 2° is approximately 6 units. The ratio of the intensities is, therefore, $22/6 \approx 3.7$.

ITQ 5 (a) $x = 3.76\,\text{m}$, $y = 1.37\,\text{m}$:

position component $x = 4\,\text{m} \times \cos 20° = 3.76\,\text{m}$

position component $y = 4\,\text{m} \times \sin 20° = 1.37\,\text{m}$

(b) $v_x = 0.78\,\text{m s}^{-1}$, $v_y = 2.90\,\text{m s}^{-1}$;

velocity component $v_x = 3\,\text{m s}^{-1} \times \cos 75° = 0.78\,\text{m s}^{-1}$

velocity component $v_y = 3\,\text{m s}^{-1} \times \sin 75° = 2.90\,\text{m s}^{-1}$

Notice that the direction of motion of the object at $t = 2\,\text{s}$ is *not* the same as its direction of motion at $t = 1\,\text{s}$.

(c) $p_x \approx 0.39\,\text{kg m s}^{-1}$, $p_y \approx 1.45\,\text{kg m s}^{-1}$:

momentum component $p_x = mv_x = 0.5\,\text{kg} \times 0.78\,\text{m s}^{-1}$

$$\approx 0.39\,\text{kg m s}^{-1}$$

momentum component $p_y = mv_y = 0.5\,\text{kg} \times 2.90\,\text{m s}^{-1}$

$$\approx 1.45\,\text{kg m s}^{-1}$$

using the answers to part (b).

ITQ 6 Nothing can be known about y at the time at which p_y is known for certain. Because, in this case, $\Delta p_y = 0$, the Heisenberg uncertainty relation $\Delta y \Delta p_y \geqslant h/4\pi$ (Equation 18a) implies that

$$\Delta y \geqslant \frac{h}{0} = \infty$$

Hence, y must be infinitely *uncertain* when p_y is known for certain.

ITQ 7 $\lambda_{\text{dB}} = 1.3 \times 10^{-35}\,\text{m}$

Using Equation 8, $\lambda_{\text{dB}} = h/mv$ (m denotes mass, v denotes speed and h is Planck's constant)

$$\lambda_{\text{dB}} = \frac{6.63 \times 10^{-34}\,\text{J s}}{(50.0\,\text{kg}) \times (1.00\,\text{m s}^{-1})}$$

i.e. $\lambda_{\text{dB}} = 1.3 \times 10^{-35}\,\text{m}$

SAQ ANSWERS AND COMMENTS

SAQ 1 The photoelectric effect is an *absorption* process: all of the incident photon's energy is transferred to the electron, and the photon 'disappears'. The Compton effect is a *scattering* process; there are two particles present both before and after the collision. The Compton effect can be understood by applying the laws of conservation of energy and momentum to the process.

SAQ 2 (a) 21°.

Using Equation 1 with $n = 1$, $\sin \theta_1 = \lambda/d$, i.e.

$$\sin \theta_1 = \frac{5.89 \times 10^{-7}\,\text{m}}{1.67 \times 10^{-6}\,\text{m}} = 0.353$$

i.e. $\theta_1 = 21°$ (to two significant figures).

(b) 0.025°.

The de Broglie wavelength λ_{dB} of the free electrons is given by Equation 8

$$\lambda_{\text{dB}} = \frac{h}{mv}$$

where h is Planck's constant and where m and v respectively denote mass and speed. For electrons with a speed of $1.00 \times 10^6\,\text{m s}^{-1}$,

$$\lambda_{\text{dB}} = \frac{6.63 \times 10^{-34}\,\text{J s}}{(9.11 \times 10^{-31}\,\text{kg}) \times (1.00 \times 10^6\,\text{m s}^{-1})}$$

$$\lambda_{\text{dB}} = 7.28 \times 10^{-10}\,\text{m}$$

The angle θ_1 at which the first diffraction maximum would be observed is given by $\sin \theta_1 = \lambda_{\text{dB}}/d$ (the wavelength λ of the radiation in the corresponding equation in part (a) has been replaced by the de Broglie wavelength λ_{dB} of the free electrons). In this case,

$$\sin \theta_1 = \frac{7.28 \times 10^{-10}\,\text{m}}{1.67 \times 10^{-6}\,\text{m}} = 4.36 \times 10^{-4}$$

i.e. $\theta_1 = 0.025°$ (to two significant figures).

Note that θ_1 for the beam of free electrons would be very much smaller than θ_1 for the beam of sodium light.

SAQ 3 (a) $6.63 \times 10^{-16}\,\text{J}$.

According to Equation 3 ($E = hf$), the energy E of each photon is

$$E = (6.63 \times 10^{-34}\,\text{J s}) \times (10^{18}\,\text{Hz})$$

$$= 6.63 \times 10^{-16}\,\text{J}$$

(b) $2.2 \times 10^{-24}\,\text{kg m s}^{-1}$ in the photon's direction of motion.

According to Equation 5, the magnitude p of the photon's momentum is given by $p = E/c$

$$p = 6.63 \times 10^{-16}\,\text{J}/(3.00 \times 10^8\,\text{m s}^{-1})$$

$$\approx 2.2 \times 10^{-24}\,\text{kg m s}^{-1}$$

using the answer to part (a). Remember that the momentum of the photon is specified by a magnitude *and* a direction (the direction is the same as the photon's direction of motion).

SAQ 4 Evidence for the wave model of electrons is provided by the experiments on *electron diffraction*. Observations of the *Compton effect* provide evidence for the particle model of electromagnetic radiation.

SAQ 5 Statements (b) and (c) are correct: quantum mechanics describes the interactions and propagation of electrons (and all other matter). Statement (a) is false because quantum mechanics does not describe visible light, or any other form of electromagnetic radiation. Statement (d) is false because quantum mechanics applies to *all* matter.

SAQ 6 (a) An individual proton is most likely to be detected around the straight-through position (zero diffraction angle) because it is there that the pattern has its most pronounced diffraction maximum.

(b) An individual proton will definitely *not* be detected at the diffraction minima, where the intensities are zero. There is *zero* probability of detecting a proton at each of these minima.

(c) The probability of detecting an individual proton with a diffraction angle of 2.2° is approximately half the probability of detecting it around the straight-through position, because the intensity when the diffraction angle is 2.2° is approximately half the intensity when the diffraction angle is zero degrees.

SAQ 7 (a) See Figure 41a, an infinite sine wave; (b) see Figure 41b, a standing wave. Note that you could have drawn *any* infinite sine wave to answer part (a) and *any* standing wave to answer part (b).

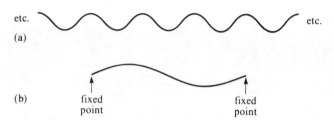

FIGURE 41   See the answer to SAQ 7.

SAQ 8 3.6×10^{-10} m.

The wavefunction of a free quantum is an infinite sine wave (Frame 3 of the AV sequence) whose wavelength is given by the de Broglie equation $\lambda_{dB} = h/mv$ (Equation 8). For an electron with the speed specified in this question

$$\lambda_{dB} = \frac{6.63 \times 10^{-34}\,\text{J s}}{(9.11 \times 10^{-31}\,\text{kg}) \times (2.00 \times 10^6\,\text{m s}^{-1})}$$

i.e. $\lambda_{dB} = 3.6 \times 10^{-10}$ m

SAQ 9 (a) Zero, because the value of the wavefunction is zero at this position. Remember from Frame 4 of the AV sequence that the probability of detecting a quantum of matter in a given small region of space is proportional to the square of the value of the wavefunction in that region.

(b) The probability of detecting the quantum at A is the same as the probability of its detection at B, because the *magnitude* of the value of the wavefunction is the same at both points, so

$$\left(\begin{array}{c}\text{value of the}\\\text{wavefunction at A}\end{array}\right)^2 = \left(\begin{array}{c}\text{value of the}\\\text{wavefunction at B}\end{array}\right)^2$$

(c) The probability of detecting the quantum at C is greater than the probability of its detection at D because the magnitude of the value of the wavefunction at C is greater than the magnitude of the value of the wavefunction at D. Hence,

$$\left(\begin{array}{c}\text{value of the}\\\text{wavefunction at C}\end{array}\right)^2 \begin{array}{c}\text{is greater}\\\text{than}\end{array} \left(\begin{array}{c}\text{value of the}\\\text{wavefunction at D}\end{array}\right)^2$$

SAQ 10   Given the degree of superficiality of the statement, it would be reasonable of you to explain the meaning of the principle in terms that do not involve components of position and momentum.

Your non-mathematical summary of the principle should go something like this: basically, it tells us about the accuracies with which position and momentum can be specified *at the same time* (the position of course specifies where something is and its momentum depends on its mass, on how quickly it is moving and on its direction of motion.) The principle tells you how to calculate the uncertainty in one of the quantities, given the uncertainty in the other quantity *at the same time*: the product of the two is *at least* equal to a tiny fixed quantity (Planck's constant divided by 4π). This implies that if one variable is known very accurately then the other variable must *at the same time* be known very inaccurately.

Note that, according to the principle, it is quite possible for *either* the position *or* the momentum to be known for certain. However, the principle says that if one of these quantities *is* known for certain, then it follows that the corresponding quantity *at the same time* is indeed infinitely uncertain. All this is, of course, a very far cry from the erroneous simplicities of the amateur philosopher's original statement!

SAQ 11 (a) $\Delta v_x = \Delta v_y = \Delta v_z \approx 6.3 \times 10^6\,\text{m s}^{-1}$.
The uncertainty Δp_x in the x-component of momentum of a quantum in the nucleus is, according to Heisenberg's uncertainty principle,

$$\Delta x \Delta p_x \geqslant \frac{h}{4\pi}$$

where Δx is the corresponding uncertainty in x and h is Planck's constant (precisely analogous formulae apply to the y- and z-components of position and momentum). The uncertainty Δx may be taken to be 5×10^{-15} m, half the diameter of the nucleus. Hence,

$$(5.00 \times 10^{-15}\,\text{m}) \times \Delta p_x \geqslant \frac{6.63 \times 10^{-34}\,\text{J s}}{4 \times 3.14}$$

i.e. $\Delta p_x \geqslant 1.06 \times 10^{-20}\,\text{kg m s}^{-1}$

The corresponding uncertainty Δv_x in the x-component of velocity is given by

$$\Delta p_x = m \Delta v_x$$

where m may be taken as the average mass of the proton and neutron (i.e. 1.67×10^{-27} kg)

$$\Delta v_x \geqslant \frac{1.06 \times 10^{-20}\,\text{kg m s}^{-1}}{1.67 \times 10^{-27}\,\text{kg}}$$

i.e. $\Delta v_x \geqslant 6.3 \times 10^6\,\text{m s}^{-1}$, 6.3 million metres per second.

By the same reasoning, Δv_y and Δv_z are also each at least $6.3 \times 10^6\,\text{m s}^{-1}$.

(b) The helium nucleus (and all other nuclei) should be visualized as a cloud whose fuzziness indicates the uncertainties in the velocity components of the constituents. Hence, an atom is visualized as an electron cloud (of diameter approximately 5×10^{-10} m) with a comparatively tiny nuclear cloud (of diameter approximately 10^{-14} m) at its centre.

SAQ 12 If there were a state of a nucleus in which a constituent proton or neutron were permanently at rest, the uncertainty in each of the momentum components of the particle would be zero so, according to the uncertainty principle, the uncertainty in the particle's position components would be infinite. This is not the case, because protons and neutrons in nuclei are normally confined to a tiny region of space (the typical nuclear diameter is approximately 10^{-14} m). Hence, there cannot exist a nuclear state in which a constituent proton or neutron is permanently at rest.

This explanation is precisely analogous to the explanation given in the text of why there is no state of an atom in which a constituent electron is permanently at rest.

SAQ 13 Given that the momentum of a free quantum is known for certain, it follows from the uncertainty principle that the position of the quantum will be infinitely uncertain. Hence, you should expect that the wavefunction of the free quantum (which, as you saw in the AV sequence, gives information about the probability of detecting it in different regions) should be of infinite extent to reflect this uncertainty in its position.

SAQ 14 (i) Each of the situations will be accounted for by quantum mechanics, which applies to *all* matter, microscopic and macroscopic.

(ii) Newtonian mechanics can be applied reliably *only* to (c) and (d), i.e. to macroscopic situations.

SAQ 15 Statement 1 is wrong because the walker will be diffracted, and the diffraction will depend on the width of the doorway, just as the diffraction of an electron by a single slit depends on the width of the slit (Section 4.2). Statement 2 is wrong because the path of the stone, which will be diffracted as it enters the well, cannot be predicted for certain just as the path of a diffracted electron cannot be predicted for certain (Section 4.2).

Note that the quantum effects specified in this answer are absolutely minute—much too small to be observed in practice.

ACKNOWLEDGEMENTS

Grateful acknowledgement is made to the following sources for permission to use material in this unit:

Figure 4(a) Photo CERN; *Figure 4(b)* Science Photo Library, London; *Figure 9* Mansell Collection, London; *Figure 14* courtesy of University of Chicago; *Figure 20* from Eisberg, R. and Resnick, R. *Quantum Physics of Atoms, Molecules, Solids, Nuclei and Particles*, © 1974, John Wiley and Sons; *Figure 21* French Embassy, London; *Figure p.22 (top right)* Austrian National Library, Vienna; *Figure 35* Camera Press, London.

INDEX FOR UNIT 30

THE OPEN UNIVERSITY
A SCIENCE FOUNDATION COURSE

UNIT 31 QUANTUM MECHANICS: ATOMS AND NUCLEI

STUDY GUIDE

This Unit, which follows on directly from Unit 30, consists of only two components—the text and a television programme.

The text will probably take you longer than average to study (the text of Unit 30 is correspondingly shorter than average). If you find that you are short of time, we suggest that you drop Section 6 and, if necessary, Section 5 as well.

The Unit's TV programme 'Quantum leaps into the atom' specifically concerns material in Sections 3.1 and 4.3 of the text. The programme can be watched with profit at any stage in your studies of the Unit.

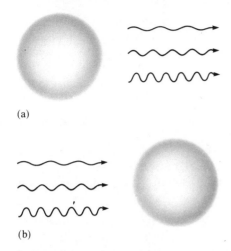

(a)

(b)

FIGURE 1   An electron in an atom can (a) emit and (b) absorb electromagnetic radiation of certain, definite wavelengths (and frequencies).

I INTRODUCTION

As you saw way back in Units 11–12, the smallest portion of each chemical element is an atom of the element. Atoms are difficult to study because they are extremely tiny—typically 0.000 000 5 millimetre in diameter—but it is possible to learn a great deal about them from the electromagnetic radiation that they emit and absorb.

One might naively expect that atoms could emit and absorb radiation of a continuous range of wavelengths but, as you know, that turns out not to be true experimentally. In the second half of the nineteenth century, it was found that the emission spectrum and the absorption spectrum of each element include radiation of certain definite wavelengths (Figure 1). Moreover, these wavelengths uniquely characterize the element—they are the element's 'fingerprint'. For example, the wavelengths of the visible radiation emitted and absorbed by atomic hydrogen are approximately 410 nm, 434 nm, 486 nm and 656 nm (Figure 2). No other element can emit or absorb visible radiation of only these four wavelengths.

wavelength   410 nm 434 nm   486 nm   656 nm

FIGURE 2   The visible emission spectrum of atomic hydrogen. (This spectrum is shown in the colour plate in Units 11–12.)

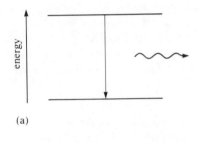

(a)

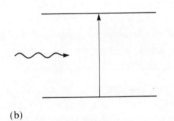

(b)

FIGURE 3   (a) When an electron in an atom makes a transition to a lower energy level, a photon is emitted with an energy equal to the spacing of the electron's energy levels; (b) an electron in an atom can absorb a photon with an energy equal to the spacing of two of the electron's energy levels, by making a transition from the lower of the two levels to the higher level.

The Danish quantum physicist Niels Bohr was the first to interpret these absorption and emission spectra in terms of *energy levels*. In 1913, Bohr correctly suggested that the electrons in an atom of each element have characteristic energy levels (definite values of energy) and that, when an electron in an atom makes a transition to a lower energy level, radiation of a clearly defined wavelength is emitted (Figure 3a). Similarly, radiation of a definite wavelength is absorbed by an electron that makes a transition to a higher energy level (Figure 3b). Hence, *radiation of certain characteristic wavelengths can be emitted and absorbed by an atom because its electrons can make transitions ('quantum leaps') only between their energy levels. The spacings between these levels are, in turn, characteristic of the atom.*

From data on the absorption or emission spectrum of an element, it is possible to deduce the spacings of the energy levels of the electrons in an atom of the element. For example, the energy levels of the electron in a hydrogen atom are shown in Figure 4: notice that *the spacings of the lowest few levels are of the order of a few electronvolts* (1 eV $\approx$ 1.602 × 10^{-19} J).

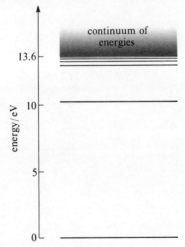

FIGURE 4   The experimentally determined energy levels of the electron in a hydrogen atom.

It was later found that the protons and neutrons in atomic *nuclei* also have energy levels: each nucleus has a characteristic set of energy levels whose spacings determine the wavelengths of the radiation that the constituent

QUANTUM NUMBER

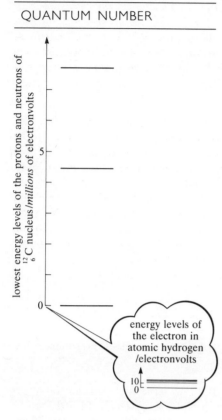

FIGURE 5 The spacings of the lowest energy levels of the protons and neutrons in a typical nucleus are generally very much wider than those of the electron in a hydrogen atom.

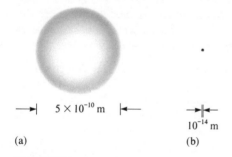

FIGURE 6 In each atom, the nucleus occupies only a tiny fraction of the atom's total volume.

protons and neutrons can emit or absorb. Experiments showed that the spacings of nuclear energy levels are generally much wider than those of electronic energy levels. As a rule of thumb, the spacings of the lowest energy levels of protons and neutrons in nuclei are approximately a million times the spacings of the lowest energy levels of the electron in atomic hydrogen (Figure 5).

So much for the results of experiments. For scientists, it is not sufficient merely to observe atomic and nuclear energy levels and to note that their spacings are very different. *Somehow, these phenomena must be understood theoretically.* It is the main purpose of this Unit to show how this understanding can be derived in terms of simple quantum mechanical ideas. We shall seek to answer four basic questions:

Q1 Why do atomic electrons have energy levels (i.e. why can't they have *any* value of energy)?

Q2 Why are the differences between the lowest energy levels of the electron in a hydrogen atom a few electronvolts?

Q3 Why do protons and neutrons in atomic nuclei have energy levels?

Q4 Why are the differences between the lowest energy levels of protons and neutrons in nuclei approximately a million times those of the electron in a hydrogen atom?

In order to give rigorous answers to these questions, the behaviour of the atoms and nuclei should be investigated using the Schrödinger equation, one of the basic equations of quantum mechanics (Unit 30). However, we cannot pursue such an investigation here because it would involve mathematics that is considerably beyond the scope of this Course. Instead, the questions will be addressed using two simple quantum mechanical models—one of the hydrogen atom, the other of a typical nucleus, which consists of protons and neutrons.

You may think that very different models are required to represent the hydrogen atom and the nucleus: after all, they do not have the same constituents and they have very different sizes (Figure 6). However, they are similar in one very important respect—they both consist of *confined* particles. The hydrogen atom consists of an electron confined to the vicinity of a proton, and a typical nucleus consists of confined protons and neutrons. As you will see shortly, this similarity enables the hydrogen atom and the typical nucleus to be modelled in very similar ways. The predictions of the models will give extremely useful insights into all four questions.

The text of this Unit has a simple structure. First, the quantum mechanical theory of confined particles is developed. This theory is then applied to the hydrogen atom using a simple model, in order to answer questions Q1 and Q2. Next, we turn to nuclei and, after revising some basic facts about nuclei that you first met in Units 11–12, questions Q3 and Q4 are answered.

Finally, we shall discuss some topics in nuclear physics—radioactive decays, fission and fusion—using Einstein's equation $E = mc^2$. In this discussion, we shall explain in simple biological terms why the products of radioactive decays can be hazardous. Also, we shall comment on how energy released in nuclear reactions can be harnessed to provide a source of electrical power.

2 QUANTUM MECHANICS OF CONFINED PARTICLES

We said in the Introduction that we shall answer questions Q1 to Q4 using quantum mechanical models of the hydrogen atom and of a typical nucleus. As you will see in Sections 3 and 4, both models concern the behaviour of a single particle confined in three dimensions. The present Section provides the theoretical basis for the models.

First, we shall consider the comparatively simple case of a particle confined in only one dimension. Then, we shall move on to consider the analogous case of a particle confined in *three* dimensions. It is this three-dimensional case that will provide the basis for the atomic and nuclear models that will be developed later.

2.1 CONFINEMENT IN ONE DIMENSION

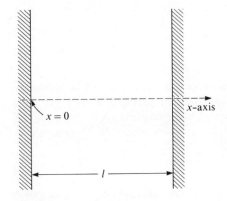

FIGURE 7 One-dimensional confinement between parallel plates.

Let's begin by considering a particle undergoing the particular type of confinement in one dimension that you first met in the AV sequence in Unit 30. Remember, the particle is confined between two infinitely high, completely impenetrable, parallel plates (Figure 7). (From now on, we shall refer to this situation more briefly as 'one-dimensional confinement between parallel plates'.)

We scarcely need to point out that the situation illustrated in Figure 7 is hypothetical. There is plainly no such thing as *infinitely* high plates, or as plates that are *completely* impenetrable. However, this artificiality is not important for our purposes: we are concerned only with the results that arise from considering the situation, because these results will be most useful later.

As you saw in Unit 30's AV sequence 'Wavefunctions of matter', one characteristic feature of the wavefunctions of a particle confined in one dimension between parallel plates is that their wavelengths are *quantized*, i.e. they can have only certain definite values. There is always a whole number of half-wavelengths between the wave's boundaries, and this condition can be expressed as an equation

$$\begin{pmatrix} \text{distance between} \\ \text{the boundaries of} \\ \text{the wavefunction} \end{pmatrix} = \text{whole number} \times \tfrac{1}{2} \begin{pmatrix} \text{wavelength} \\ \text{of the} \\ \text{wavefunction} \end{pmatrix} \qquad (1)$$

The whole number (which could be 1 or 2 or 3 ... etc.) is called the **quantum number** of the wavefunction and it is denoted by n. Hence, if the wavelength of the wavefunction associated with quantum number n is $(\lambda_{wf})_n$ and if the distance between the boundaries of the wavefunction is l (Figure 8), Equation 1 becomes

$$l = n \times \tfrac{1}{2}(\lambda_{wf})_n \qquad (2)$$

Equation 2 implies that

$$(\lambda_{wf})_n = \frac{2l}{n}, \text{ where } n = 1 \text{ or } 2 \text{ or } 3 \dots \text{ etc.} \qquad (3)$$

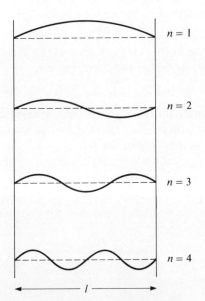

FIGURE 8 Four wavefunctions of a particle confined in one dimension between parallel plates (Figure 7).

Equation 3 is a simple expression for the quantized wavelengths $(\lambda_{wf})_n$ of the wavefunctions of a particle confined in one dimension between parallel plates. The equation enables the allowed wavelengths to be calculated very easily; for example, if $l = 10^{-2}$ m, the two longest allowed wavelengths (which correspond to $n = 1$ and $n = 2$) of the wavefunctions are

$$\text{for } n = 1, \quad (\lambda_{wf})_1 = \frac{2 \times 10^{-2}\,\text{m}}{1} = 2 \times 10^{-2}\,\text{m}$$

$$\text{for } n = 2, \quad (\lambda_{wf})_2 = \frac{2 \times 10^{-2}\,\text{m}}{2} = 10^{-2}\,\text{m}$$

We shall now show that because the wavelengths of the wavefunctions are quantized (Equation 3), it follows that the total energy of the particle is also quantized, i.e. that the particle has energy levels. The link between the wavelengths of the wavefunctions and the particle's energy values can be made using de Broglie's formula.

QUANTIZATION

ENERGY LEVELS

STUDY COMMENT The following derivation of the particle's energy levels is important and you should work through it carefully. However, you are *not* required to commit it to memory.

In Unit 30, you saw that according to de Broglie's formula, the de Broglie wavelength λ_{dB} of a free particle with momentum of magnitude p is given by

$$\lambda_{dB} = \frac{h}{p} \tag{4}$$

where h is Planck's constant, approximately 6.626×10^{-34} J s. Since p is defined by the expression $p = mv$, where m is the mass of the particle and v is its speed (Unit 3),

$$\lambda_{dB} = \frac{h}{mv} \tag{5}$$

Now let us suppose that this equation, which strictly speaking applies *only* to free particles, can be applied to the confined particle that we are considering*. Also, suppose that each allowed wavelength $(\lambda_{wf})_n$ of the confined particle's wavefunctions is equal to the corresponding de Broglie wavelength λ_{dB}:

$$(\lambda_{wf})_n = \lambda_{dB} \tag{6}$$

Since $(\lambda_{wf})_n = 2l/n$ (Equation 3) and $\lambda_{dB} = h/mv$ (Equation 5), Equation 6 implies that

$$\frac{2l}{n} = \frac{h}{mv} \tag{7}$$

where $n = 1$ or 2 or $3 \ldots$ etc. When Equation 7 is rearranged, we find

$$v = \frac{nh}{2ml} \tag{8}$$

Because h, m and l are constant for a given particle confined between a given pair of plates, Equation 8 predicts that the speed v of the particle is quantized. The allowed values of v correspond to the whole-number values of n: when $n = 1$, $v = h/(2ml)$; when $n = 2$, $v = 2h/(2ml)$; etc.

It is now quite straightforward to find the kinetic energy values of the particle. The kinetic energy E_k of a particle with mass m and speed v is given by

$$E_k = \tfrac{1}{2}mv^2 \tag{9}$$

as you saw in Unit 9. If we now substitute into this equation the expression for the speed v of the confined particle (when it is described by the wavefunction characterized by the quantum number n), we find

$$(E_k)_n = \tfrac{1}{2}m\left(\frac{nh}{2ml}\right)^2$$

i.e. $$(E_k)_n = \tfrac{1}{2}m\frac{n^2h^2}{4m^2l^2}$$

i.e. $$(E_k)_n = \frac{n^2h^2}{8ml^2}, \quad \text{where} \quad n = 1 \text{ or } 2 \text{ or } 3 \ldots \text{etc.} \tag{10}$$

---

* You may think that the de Broglie formula cannot be applied to the confined particle because such an application would imply that the momentum of the particle were known with perfect accuracy, in contradiction with the uncertainty principle ($\Delta x \Delta p_x \geqslant h/(4\pi)$, Unit 30). However, this objection is not valid: it is assumed in the derivation that the *magnitude* p of the particle's momentum is known precisely, but the *direction* in which the particle is travelling has not been specified. Hence, there *is* an uncertainty in the x-component of the particle's x-component of momentum. This uncertainty Δp_x has the value p: the x-component of momentum would be $p_x = +p$ if the particle is travelling in one direction and $p_x = -p$ if it is travelling in the opposite direction, so the 'spread' of p_x is $p - (-p) = 2p$, and so $\Delta p_x = p$ (half the spread).

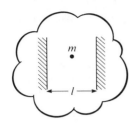

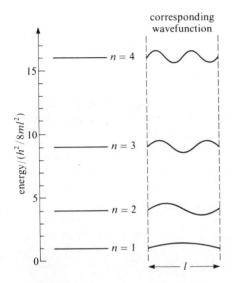

FIGURE 9 The four lowest energy levels and the corresponding wavefunctions of a particle confined in one dimension between parallel plates (Figure 7).

The particle is free to move between the plates so its energy depends only on its speed, not on its position. The energy that the particle has because of its position—its *potential* energy—is therefore a constant. The value of this constant may be taken to be zero (remember from Unit 9 that only *relative* values of energy are important, not absolute values). Hence, the *total* energy E of the particle (when it is described by the wavefunction characterized by the quantum number n) is given by the right-hand side of Equation 10

$$E_n = \frac{n^2 h^2}{8ml^2}, \quad \text{where} \quad n = 1 \text{ or } 2 \text{ or } 3 \dots \text{etc.} \tag{11}$$

This is the result we have been seeking: it gives the total energy values of a particle confined in one dimension between parallel plates. Because the quantum number n is a whole number, it follows that the quantity n^2 in Equation 11 is also a whole number. Each value of n therefore corresponds to a certain, definite value of total energy E: when $n = 1$, $E_1 = h^2/(8ml^2)$; when $n = 2$, $E_2 = 4h^2/(8ml^2)$ and so on. The energy is therefore **quantized**—the particle has **energy levels**.

The underlying reason for the quantization of the particle's energy is that a *whole* number of half-wavelengths of the particle's wavefunctions have to 'fit' between the confining plates (Equation 1). It is because the particle is *confined* that its energy is quantized.

The lowest four energy levels of a particle confined in one dimension are shown in Figure 9, together with its corresponding wavefunctions. Remember that these energy levels and wavefunctions apply *only* to a particle that can move in only one dimension between parallel plates.

It is worthwhile to pause briefly to examine further the energy levels of the particle. First, consider its lowest possible energy. According to commonsense ideas, it should be expected that the minimum energy of the particle should be zero—this would be the energy of the particle when it is permanently stationary between the plates. However, according to Figure 9 the particle cannot have zero total energy—the particle's lowest possible energy is $h^2/(8ml^2)$. This is the total energy of the particle when the minimum number (i.e. one) of half-wavelengths of its wavefunctions 'fits' between the plates.

Now consider the transitions that the particle can make between its energy levels. If the particle makes a transition to a lower energy level, its energy decreases and this energy is 'carried off' by a single emitted photon. For example, if the particle makes a transition from the $n = 3$ energy level, $E_3 = 9h^2/(8ml^2)$, to the $n = 2$ energy level, $E_2 = 4h^2/(8ml^2)$, it will emit a single photon with an energy given by the difference between the two energies, which we can label $\Delta E_{3 \to 2}$:

$$\Delta E_{3 \to 2} = \frac{9h^2}{8ml^2} - \frac{4h^2}{8ml^2}$$

i.e. $\quad \Delta E_{3 \to 2} = \frac{5h^2}{8ml^2} \tag{12}$

(Figure 10). The radiation emitted of course has a characteristic frequency and wavelength.

☐ What is the *frequency* $f_{3 \to 2}$ of the radiation emitted in the transition from $n = 3$ to $n = 2$ shown in Figure 10?

■ The standard formula $E = hf$ for the energy of a photon, implies in this case that $\Delta E_{3 \to 2} = hf_{3 \to 2}$, so according to Equation 12

$$\frac{5h^2}{8ml^2} = hf_{3 \to 2}$$

i.e. $\quad f_{3 \to 2} = \frac{5h}{8ml^2} \tag{13}$

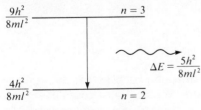

FIGURE 10 When a particle makes a transition from the energy level $9h^2/(8ml^2)$ to the lower energy level $4h^2/(8ml^2)$, a single photon with energy $5h^2/(8ml^2)$ is emitted.

DEGENERACY

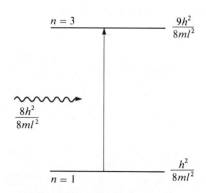

FIGURE 11   When a particle that occupies the energy level $h^2/(8ml^2)$ absorbs a photon with energy $8h^2/(8ml^2)$, the particle makes a transition to the higher energy level $9h^2/(8ml^2)$.

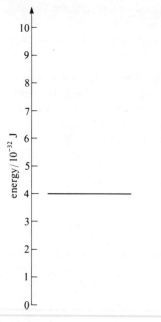

FIGURE 12   See ITQ 2.

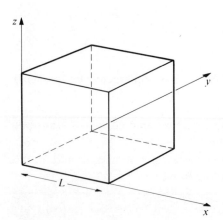

FIGURE 13   A hollow cube whose sides each have length L and whose faces are impenetrable.

□ What is the *wavelength* $\lambda_{3\to2}$ of the radiation emitted in the transition shown in Figure 10?

■ The standard relationship $c = f\lambda$ between the frequency f and wavelength λ of electromagnetic radiation (c is the speed of light in a vacuum) implies in this case that

$$\lambda_{3\to2} = \frac{c}{f_{3\to2}} \tag{14}$$

Hence, Equations 13 and 14 imply that

$$\lambda_{3\to2} = \frac{8ml^2 c}{5h} \tag{15}$$

Remember that these expressions for frequency $f_{3\to2}$ and wavelength $\lambda_{3\to2}$ of the emitted radiation apply specifically to the transition from $n = 3$ to $n = 2$ shown in Figure 10. The values of frequency and wavelength for the radiation emitted in other transitions must of course be calculated separately, by considering the difference between the energy levels involved.

The particle can also make a transition to a higher energy level by absorbing a photon of electromagnetic radiation. For this to happen, the photon must have an energy that is exactly equal to the difference in energy between the energy levels concerned. For example (Figure 11), the particle can make a transition from the $n = 1$ energy level, $E_1 = h^2/(8ml^2)$, to the $n = 3$ energy level, $E_3 = 9h^2/(8ml^2)$, by absorbing a photon with an energy $\Delta E_{1\to3}$ where

$$\Delta E_{1\to3} = \frac{9h^2}{8ml^2} - \frac{h^2}{8ml^2} \quad \text{i.e.} \quad \Delta E_{1\to3} = \frac{8h^2}{8ml^2}$$

Now, before you move on to Section 2.2, which concerns confinement in *three* dimensions, have a go at ITQs 1 and 2 in order to check that you have understood the important points covered so far.

ITQ 1   Explain in a few sentences (*without* using equations) why, according to quantum mechanics, a particle confined in one dimension between parallel plates has energy levels.

ITQ 2   A particle that has a mass of 1.25×10^{-27} kg is confined in one dimension between parallel plates that are separated by 6.63×10^{-5} m.

(a) Using Equation 11, show that the energy levels of the particle are given by

$$E_n = (10^{-32}\,\text{J}) \times n^2$$

where n is a whole number ($n = 1$ or 2 or 3 ... etc.)

(b) Show on Figure 12 the $n = 1$ and $n = 3$ energy levels of the particle (the $n = 2$ energy level is already shown).

(c) What is the energy of the photon of electromagnetic radiation that is emitted when the particle makes a transition from the $n = 3$ energy level to the $n = 1$ energy level?

(d) What are the frequency and wavelength of the radiation emitted in the transition specified in part (c)?

2.2 CONFINEMENT IN THREE DIMENSIONS

In Section 2.1, we discussed the confinement of a particle that can move in only one dimension between parallel plates. We shall now consider an analogous situation in which a particle can move in *three* dimensions in a hollow cube (Figure 13) whose sides (of length L) are completely impenetrable, so that the particle can never escape. Because the motion of the particle is three-dimensional, it follows by definition that the position of the particle can be specified with respect to *three* axes (x, y and z in Figure 13).

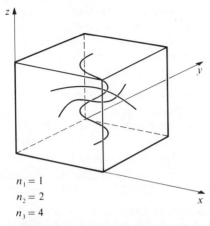

$n_1 = 1$
$n_2 = 2$
$n_3 = 4$

FIGURE 14   For a particle confined in a hollow cube (Figure 13), a whole number of half-wavelengths of the particle's wavefunction 'fit' between each pair of the cube's faces. In the particular case of the wavefunction shown schematically here, one half-wavelength 'fits' between one pair of faces, two half-wavelengths 'fit' between another pair, and four half-wavelengths 'fit' between the remaining pair.

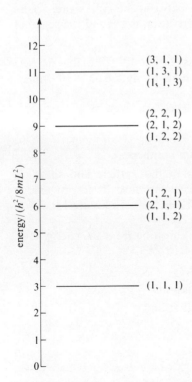

FIGURE 15   The four lowest energy levels of a particle of mass m confined in a cube whose sides each have length L.

According to quantum mechanics, the behaviour of any particle is determined by its wavefunction. For a particle that can move in three dimensions, its possible wavefunctions are very difficult to visualize properly. However, the quantum mechanical principles of confinement in three dimensions are practically identical with those that underlie the theory of one-dimensional confinement. You saw in Section 2.1 that, in the case of one-dimensional motion, a whole number of half-wavelengths of the particle's wavefunction must 'fit' between the plates (for a given wavefunction, this whole number is given by its quantum number n). This quantization of particle's associated wavelength led directly to the quantization of the particle's energy.

In the case of the three-dimensional motion of a particle in a cube, a whole number of half-wavelengths of the particle's wavefunctions must 'fit' between *each* of three pairs of opposite faces of the cube (an example is illustrated schematically in Figure 14). Hence, the wavefunction is characterized by three quantum numbers n_1, n_2 and n_3, which give respectively the number of half-wavelengths of the wavefunctions that fit in the x-, y- and z- directions (Figure 14). Each of these quantum numbers can equal any whole number.

The quantization of the wavelengths of the particle leads to the quantization of its energy. It can be shown that the energy of any particle of mass m confined in a cube with sides of length L is given by

$$E = \frac{n_1{}^2 h^2}{8mL^2} + \frac{n_2{}^2 h^2}{8mL^2} + \frac{n_3{}^2 h^2}{8mL^2} \tag{16}$$

It would have been more logical (and more consistent with the notation used in Equation 11) if we had denoted this energy by E_{n_1, n_2, n_3}, but that notation would have been just *too* cumbersome!

Because n_1, n_2 and n_3 in Equation 16 are whole numbers, it follows that the total energy E of the particle can have only certain, definite values: the particle's energy is quantized. Notice the similarity between Equation 16 (which concerns *three*-dimensional confinement) and Equation 11 ($E_n = n^2 h^2 / 8ml^2$), the corresponding expression for *one*-dimensional confinement.

It is convenient to re-express Equation 16, by taking out the common factor $h^2/(8mL^2)$ from each of the three terms in the equation:

$$E = \frac{h^2}{8mL^2}(n_1{}^2 + n_2{}^2 + n_3{}^2) \quad \begin{array}{l} n_1 = 1 \text{ or } 2 \text{ or } 3 \ldots \text{etc.} \\[4pt] n_2 = 1 \text{ or } 2 \text{ or } 3 \ldots \text{etc.} \\[4pt] n_3 = 1 \text{ or } 2 \text{ or } 3 \ldots \text{etc.} \end{array} \tag{17}$$

This equation (identical in content with Equation 16, but more tidily expressed) is extremely important and it will be used frequently in this Unit. However, there is no need for you to memorize it.

Figure 15 shows the lowest few energy levels of the particle confined in a cube. As you can see from the Figure, some energy levels of the particle in the cube correspond to more than one set of quantum numbers (n_1, n_2, n_3). For example, the energy level $E = 6h^2/(8mL^2)$ corresponds to three different wavefunctions: the ones specified by $(n_1 = 1, n_2 = 2, n_3 = 1)$, $(n_1 = 2, n_2 = 1, n_3 = 1)$ and $(n_1 = 1, n_2 = 1, n_3 = 2)$. This phenomenon, in which an energy level corresponds to more than one wavefunction, is called **degeneracy**. The wavefunctions that correspond to the energy level are said to be *degenerate*.

ITQ 3   (a) What is the energy of a particle of mass m in a cube with sides of length L when the particle's wavefunction is characterized by the quantum numbers $n_1 = 2, n_2 = 2, n_3 = 2$? Show this energy level on Figure 15.

(b) Is the energy level $E = 9h^2/(8mL^2)$ shown in Figure 15 degenerate? Explain your answer briefly.

Because the energy of a particle confined in a cube is quantized, it follows that the particle can emit and absorb radiation of only certain definite wavelengths. For a given transition, the wavelength of the radiation is, of course, determined by the energy difference between the energy levels concerned.

That concludes this quantum mechanical discussion of confined particles. We have considered theoretically two special (and highly artificial!) situations—a particle confined between parallel plates and in a cube. The crucial point to remember is that in both cases the *confinement* of the particle has implied that the energy of the particle is *quantized*, i.e. that the particle has energy levels.

In the next two Sections, these somewhat abstract concepts will be used when we formulate models of the hydrogen atom and a typical nucleus. All the abstract theoretical work you have done in this Section will be handsomely rewarded shortly when we use our models to account for data from experiments.

SUMMARY OF SECTION 2

1   The energy levels of a particle of mass m confined in one dimension between infinite, parallel, impenetrable plates that are separated by distance l are given in the usual notation by

$$E_n = \frac{n^2 h^2}{8ml^2} \tag{11}*$$

This expression is derived by 'fitting' a whole number of half-wavelengths of the particle's wavefunctions between the boundaries (i.e. the plates).

2   The energy levels of a particle of mass m confined in three dimensions in a hollow cube (with impenetrable sides of length L) are given in the usual notation by

$$E = \frac{h^2}{8mL^2} (n_1^2 + n_2^2 + n_3^2) \tag{17}*$$

This expression can be derived by 'fitting' a whole number of half-wavelengths of the particle's wavefunctions between the cube's three pairs of faces (e.g. Figure 14). However, such a derivation is beyond the scope of this Course.

SAQs 1 and 2 concern a particle of mass 1.25×10^{-28} kg that is permanently confined in a cube whose sides each have length 6.63×10^{-6} m.

SAQ 1   (a) Show that the particle's energy levels are given by

$$E = 10^{-29} \text{J} \times (n_1^2 + n_2^2 + n_3^2)$$

where n_1, n_2 and n_3 are the particle's quantum numbers.

(b) Calculate the four lowest energy levels of the particle and show on Figure 16 the three energy levels of the particle above its lowest energy level, which is already shown on the Figure. (Hint: refer to Figure 15).

SAQ 2   Suppose that the particle makes a transition from the energy level $E = 11 \times 10^{-29}$ J to the energy level $E = 6 \times 10^{-29}$ J.

(a) What is the energy of the emitted photon?

(b) What is the frequency of the emitted radiation?

(c) What is the wavelength of the emitted radiation?

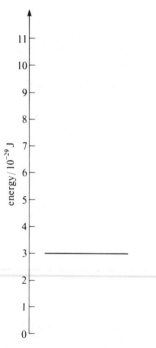

FIGURE 16   See SAQs 1 and 2.

3 UNDERSTANDING ATOMIC ENERGY LEVELS

In this Section, the theoretical ideas introduced in the previous Section will be used to derive insights into atomic energy levels. First, the atom with the simplest possible structure—the hydrogen atom—will be considered in detail. A model of this atom will be formulated and the predictions of the model will be compared with the corresponding data from experiments. Finally, we shall look at more advanced atomic models.

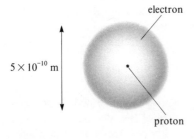

FIGURE 17 A visualization of a hydrogen atom.

3.1 A SIMPLE MODEL OF THE HYDROGEN ATOM (TV programme)

A hydrogen atom has a diameter of approximately 5×10^{-10} m and it consists of an electron moving around a proton (Figure 17). The charge of the electron, approximately -1.602×10^{-19} C, is exactly opposite to that of the proton so the atom has no net electrical charge. Coulomb's law of electrostatics (Unit 9) tells us that the magnitude of the attractive electrostatic force F_{el} between the electron and the proton varies with their separation r

$$F_{el} \propto \frac{1}{r^2} \tag{18}$$

The separation r of the two particles varies continuously, so the electrostatic force between the electron and the proton also changes continuously. There is also an attractive gravitational force between the two particles but its magnitude is negligible compared with that of the electrostatic force.

Experiments show that hydrogen atoms emit and absorb radiation of certain, definite wavelengths and this tells us that the energy of the atom is *quantized*. How can this energy quantization be understood theoretically?

It would be difficult to understand this phenomenon using a *complete* description of the atom, because such a description would have to take into account not only the masses, charges and spins of its constituent particles, but also the continuously changing electrostatic force between the electron and the proton. Such an investigation will not be attempted here as it would be beyond the scope of this Course. Instead, the energy of the electron in a hydrogen atom will be studied using a *model* of the atom.

Before the model is described in detail, it is worthwhile to pause to review the meaning of the term 'model'. In Unit 1, it was defined to be 'an artificial construction invented to represent or to simulate the properties, the behaviour, or the relationship between the individual parts of the real entity being studied'. The 'real entity' that is being studied here is the hydrogen atom, which we shall represent by the model shown in Figure 18. The atom is modelled as a hollow cubic box (with sides of 5.00×10^{-10} m, approximately the diameter of the atom) containing a particle with the same mass as the electron (approximately 9.11×10^{-31} kg). By representing the hydrogen atom in this way, only two of its characteristics are being taken into account:

o its size;

o the mass of its constituent electron.

You have probably already guessed why we have chosen this particular model: in Section 2, the confinement of a particle in a cubic box has already been discussed. Hence, in choosing this model, we can use results that have already been derived. The model is chosen for its simplicity and convenience.

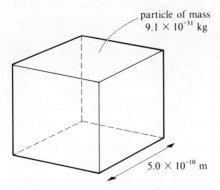

FIGURE 18 A simple model of the hydrogen atom.

It is important to bear in mind that, in the formulation of the model, some simplifying assumptions have been made. For example, the physical presence of the proton in the atom is ignored and it is assumed that the atom has the shape of a cube. The way in which the magnitude of the attractive electrostatic force between the proton and the electron depends on their separation has not been taken into account. Also, the spin of the electron has been ignored. (Experiments also show that the proton has spin, but that is also disregarded.)

You may well be thinking that some or all of these assumptions are unreasonable. It is indeed only prudent to be wary of the validity of each assumption in this (or any other) model, but it is also wise to defer judgement on the model until its predictions have been compared with the corresponding experimental results. Only after the comparison has been made is it reasonable to assess the model's worth. If its predictions turn out to be in flagrant conflict with data, then the model must be dropped and another should be formulated. Alternatively, if the predictions are found to be in good agreement with experiment, it would be reasonable to make the modifications necessary to improve the agreement.

ITQ 4   What would you consider to be *reasonable* agreement between the predictions of the model for the energy values of the atom and the experimentally determined values? For example, do you think it reasonable to expect the two to agree exactly?

(This is really a personal question—only you can say what you consider to be a reasonable outcome of the comparison. However, there are some important points to bear in mind when answering an open-ended question like this: don't forget to look at our answer before you move on!)

Now, at last, it is time to apply the model. We shall compare the energy values predicted by the model of the hydrogen atom with the energy levels of atomic hydrogen that are observed experimentally.

First, consider the model (Figure 18): the hydrogen atom is represented by a particle of mass 9.11×10^{-31} kg confined in a hollow cube, whose sides each are of length 5.00×10^{-10} m. Note that these input data are given to three significant figures; at the end of the calculation we shall 'round down' the predictions to *two* significant figures (remember the last significant figure is always unreliable).

You know from Section 2 that a particle of mass m in a cube whose sides have length L has *energy levels* given by

$$E = \frac{h^2}{8mL^2} (n_1{}^2 + n_2{}^2 + n_3{}^2) \tag{17}*$$

where n_1, n_2, n_3 are each separately equal to a whole number. Here, immediately, is a success of the model: it predicts that the energy of the system it represents—the hydrogen atom—is quantized, in agreement with experimental observations. The particle in the cube has energy levels because it is confined, so it is reasonable to infer that the *electron in a hydrogen atom has energy levels because it is confined.*

Let us now examine the *numerical* predictions of the model. Because Planck's constant $h \approx 6.63 \times 10^{-34}$ J s and because $m = 9.11 \times 10^{-31}$ kg and $L = 5.00 \times 10^{-10}$ m in the model, Equation 17 says that the energy levels of the particle in the box are given by

$$E = \frac{(6.63 \times 10^{-34} \,\text{J s})^2}{8 \times (9.11 \times 10^{-31}\,\text{kg}) \times (5.00 \times 10^{-10}\,\text{m})^2} (n_1{}^2 + n_2{}^2 + n_3{}^2) \tag{19}$$

It is straightforward to show that

$$E = (2.41 \times 10^{-19}\,\text{J}) \times (n_1{}^2 + n_2{}^2 + n_3{}^2) \tag{20}$$

(You should check with your calculator that Equation 20 follows from Equation 19.) As you saw in Unit 9, it is convenient in atomic science to measure energy in units of electronvolts (eV) rather than in the standard units of joules (J):

$$1\,\text{eV} \approx 1.602 \times 10^{-19}\,\text{J} \tag{21}$$

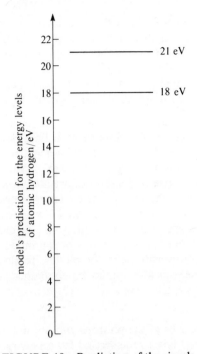

FIGURE 19 Prediction of the simple model of the hydrogen atom (Figure 18) for the six lowest energy levels of atomic hydrogen. In ITQ 5, you are asked to draw in the four lowest energy levels.

Hence, using Equation 21, Equation 20 can be re-expressed, to two significant figures, as

$$E = 1.5\,\text{eV} \times (n_1{}^2 + n_2{}^2 + n_3{}^2) \tag{22}$$

Equation 22 gives the energy levels of the particle in the box—*the equation is the model's prediction for the energy levels of the electron in a hydrogen atom.*

ITQ 5 Calculate the four lowest energy levels of the particle and mark them on Figure 19 (the two energy levels above the lowest four are already marked on the Figure). (Hint: it may help you to look back to Figure 15).

The spacings of the four lowest energy levels of the electron in the hydrogen atom predicted by the model (Figure 19) are compared in Figure 20 with the experimentally determined spacings. Notice that in Figure 20 the lowest energy levels are aligned. This alignment can be made because the *numerical* values associated with the levels are not important, because *absolute* energy values cannot be measured; only their *differences* can be measured (e.g. from atomic hydrogen's emission spectrum and absorption spectrum). Thus, as you saw in Unit 9, only the *relative* values of energies are important.

As you can see from Figure 20, the agreement between the model and experiment is remarkably good—the spacings of the lowest levels agree to well within an order of magnitude. For higher energy levels, the comparison is not so successful: the model predicts that there are an infinite number of energy levels that correspond to the infinite number of possible values of $n_1{}^2 + n_2{}^2 + n_3{}^2$ in Equation 22 (remember n_1, n_2 and n_3 can each equal any positive number). However, experiment shows that the electron in a hydrogen atom has a continuum (i.e. a *continuous*, non-quantized range) of energies, starting approximately 13.6 eV above the lowest energy level. The model cannot account for this because when the electron has an energy in the continuum of energies, it is *not* confined. Such a situation cannot be described within the scope of the model, according to which the electron is always confined.

The prediction for the spacings of the lowest few energy levels was successful because the model took into account the three factors that are most important in determining the spacings of the energy levels—the size of the atom, the mass of the confined electron and the value of Planck's constant. This answers question Q2 in the Introduction: *the differences between the lowest few energy levels of the electron in a hydrogen atom (roughly a few electronvolts) are determined mainly by the size of the atom, by the mass of the electron and by the value of Planck's constant.*

FIGURE 20 Comparison between the model's prediction for the four lowest energy levels of atomic hydrogen and the experimentally determined energy levels of atomic hydrogen. The lowest energy levels have been aligned—this can be done because only *relative* energies (not their actual numerical values) are important. In other words, the position of the zero of energy is arbitrary (Unit 9).

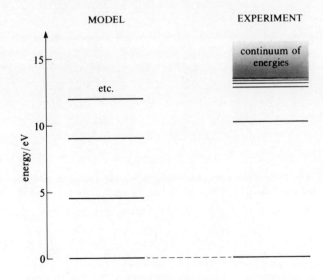

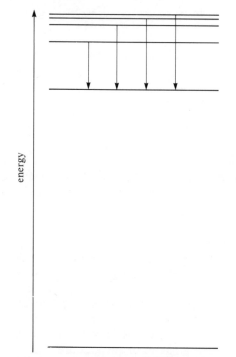

FIGURE 21 The transitions that are found experimentally to be responsible for the four *visible* spectral lines of atomic hydrogen.

It is a useful exercise to compare the model's numerical predictions for the energies of the photons emitted from atomic hydrogen with the corresponding experimental data. We now want you to carry out this exercise in order that you can see how well the model accounts for the visible part of the spectrum of atomic hydrogen, which is studied in part of the physics experiment at Summer School (and in the Fraunhofer spectrum experiment in Units 11–12).

The visible spectrum of atomic hydrogen consists of four spectral lines that have wavelengths of approximately 656 nm, 486 nm, 434 nm and 410 nm, and these respectively correspond to photon energies of 1.9 eV, 2.6 eV, 2.9 eV and 3.0 eV. The transitions that give rise to these lines are shown in Figure 21: they correspond to transitions to the second lowest energy level from the third, fourth, fifth and sixth lowest energy levels. In ITQ 6, you will see how well the measured values of the energies of the photons emitted in these transitions agree with the corresponding predictions of the model. It will be assumed that the corresponding transitions in the model are also to the second lowest energy level from the four levels immediately higher in energy (Table 1).

ITQ 6 (a) Use Figure 19 to find the energies of the photons emitted in the transitions of the particle in the atom-sized box to the second lowest energy level from the third, fourth, fifth and sixth lowest energy levels. Enter your results in the spaces provided in Table 1.

(b) Do you think that the agreement between the predictions of the model and the corresponding measurements is good enough for the model to be regarded as useful?

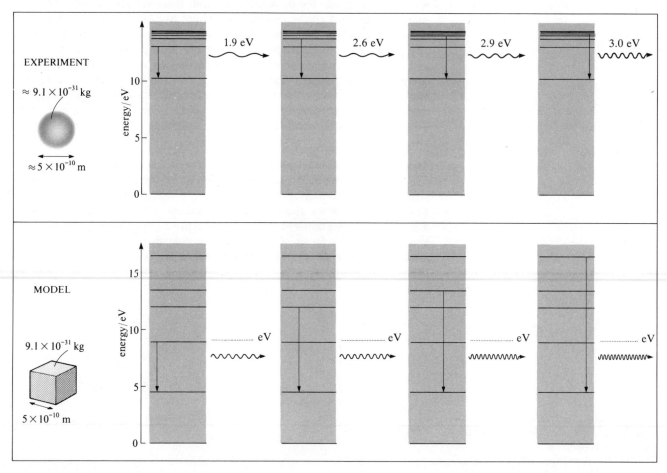

TABLE 1 The transitions associated with the visible emission spectrum of atomic hydrogen, compared with the corresponding transitions between energy levels predicted by the particle-in-a-box model of the hydrogen atom

3.2 MORE ADVANCED ATOMIC MODELS

It would be wrong to leave you with the impression that the most advanced theoretical descriptions of atoms involve modelling them as cubes—such an impression would be very misleading. Modern theoretical treatments are very much more subtle and complicated than our particle-in-a-box model.

It is possible to give a very good account of energy levels of the electron in a hydrogen atom (and of the corresponding wavefunctions) using the Schrödinger equation (Unit 30). According to this equation, the wavefunction of an electron in a hydrogen atom can be characterized by three quantum numbers—the principal quantum number n, the second quantum number l and the orbital magnetic quantum number m_l*. *Note that these quantum numbers have nothing to do with the quantum numbers n_1, n_2, n_3 of a particle confined in a cubic box.*

You met the quantum numbers n, l and m_l in Units 11–12, where you saw that each set of quantum numbers corresponds to a particular electron orbital, which gives the probability of detecting in each region the electron when it has a given set of quantum numbers (e.g. Figure 22). Each orbital can be calculated using the Schrödinger equation.

FIGURE 22   The orbital of the electron in a hydrogen atom when the electron has the lowest possible energy.

So much for the energy levels of the electron in a hydrogen atom; what about the energies of electrons in heavy atoms (i.e. atoms that contain more than one electron)? In common with the hydrogen atom, heavy atoms have energy levels—quantized values of energy—and this quantization can be understood intuitively by considering the atoms' constituent electrons. Because these electrons are *confined*, they have energy levels. The differences between the energy levels of heavy atoms cannot be predicted as easily as those of atomic hydrogen, because in a heavy atom there are complex mutual interactions of the electrons moving around the nucleus. (No such complexities occur in the hydrogen atom, of course, because it contains only *one* electron.) The mutual interactions can be taken into account only by using computers to apply the Schrödinger equation to the electrons. When this is done it is possible to predict energy levels and wavefunctions with high accuracy.

The results of calculations of this kind show that the orbitals of heavy atoms broadly resemble those of hydrogen, but there are important differences between the energies of electrons in hydrogen and in heavy atoms. First, the higher charge of the nuclei of heavy atoms ensures that the inner electrons are held more tightly than is the electron in a hydrogen atom. Second, the energy levels of electrons with the same principal quantum number n are no longer degenerate as they are in hydrogen (Units 11–12) but depend on the second quantum number l. Electrons with the same values of the principal quantum number n and the second quantum number l, but different values of m_l, have approximately the same energies. The

* The spin magnetic quantum number, and indeed the actual phenomenon of electron spin, can be understood only by using quantum mechanics in conjunction with the special theory of relativity.

NUCLEUS

MASS NUMBER

ATOMIC NUMBER

result is that the energy level diagram for a heavy atom, such as the sodium atom, contains more levels of *different* energies than that of hydrogen, and the spacings between the lowest levels are greater than the corresponding spacings in the energy level diagram for hydrogen (Figure 23).

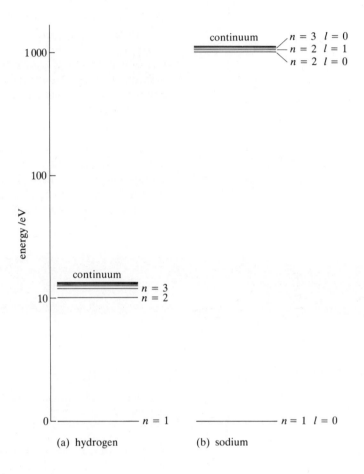

FIGURE 23   Electron energy-level diagrams for (a) hydrogen and (b) sodium. Note that the energy scale is logarithmic, to accommodate the large values for sodium.

As a result of the spacings of the energy levels, spectra of the outermost electrons of heavy atoms are observed in the visible and ultraviolet regions of the electromagnetic spectrum. Spectra involving the most tightly bound electrons of heavy atoms (e.g. $n = 1$), are observed in the X-ray region of the electromagnetic spectrum.

SUMMARY OF SECTION 3

1   The hydrogen atom was modelled as a particle in a cubic box. In the model, the mass of the particle is taken to be 9.11×10^{-31} kg (approximately the same as that of the electron) and each side of box is taken to be of length 5.00×10^{-10} m (approximately the same as the diameter of the hydrogen atom).

2   The model gave insights into the energy of the electron in the hydrogen atom. First, the energy is *quantized* because the electron is confined. Second, the differences between the electron's lowest few energy levels (roughly a few electronvolts) are determined principally by the size of the atom, by the mass of the electron and by the value of Planck's constant.

3   The differences between the lowest energy levels of electrons in heavy atoms (i.e. atoms that contain more than one electron) are greater than the corresponding differences for the energy levels of atomic hydrogen.

4   Models based on the Schrödinger equation allow electronic energy levels and wavefunctions for atoms to be predicted with high accuracy.

SAQ 3 In this question, you are asked to comment on the formulation and application of the particle-in-a-box model of the hydrogen atom used in this Section.

(a) Why did we formulate the model? Why didn't we use a more complete description of the hydrogen atom?

(b) Wasn't it ridiculous to use a model that is based on the assumption that the hydrogen atom has the shape of a cube?

(c) The prediction of the model for the energy levels of the electron in the hydrogen atom is certainly not in perfect agreement with experiment (Figure 20). Does this disagreement prove that the model is worthless?

SAQ 4 In a nutshell, what were the two key insights about the hydrogen atom that were derived from the particle-in-a-box model?

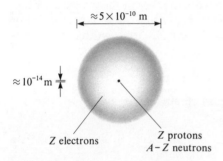

FIGURE 24 An atom contains Z electrons, Z protons and $A - Z$ neutrons, where Z is the atomic number of the nucleus and A is its mass number.

4 THE ATOMIC NUCLEUS

Atomic nuclei were first discussed in Units 11–12, where you saw that the **nucleus** is the tiny, positively charged core of the atom. Apart from the hydrogen nucleus $^1_1$H, which consists of a single proton, nuclei generally consist of both protons and neutrons (Figure 24).

In this Section, several aspects of basic nuclear physics will be discussed. First, the material on nuclei that you met in Units 11–12 will be revised. Second, we shall consider the type of interaction that holds together the protons and neutrons in nuclei. Third, a particle-in-a-box model will be used to try to understand why the energy spacings of the lowest energy levels of nuclei are very much wider than those of the electron in the hydrogen atom. The energy required to break apart atomic nuclei will then be considered, and the Section is concluded by a discussion of nuclear masses in which Einstein's equation $E = mc^2$ is introduced.

4.1 THE CONTENTS OF NUCLEI

The diameter of each nucleus is approximately 10^{-14} m (a hundredth of a millionth of a millionth of a metre), which is very small indeed compared with the typical diameter of an atom, approximately 5×10^{-10} m (Figure 24). The nucleus occupies proportionately about as much space in an atom as a pinhead inside Wembley stadium.

The two types of particle in the nucleus—the proton and the neutron—have approximately the same mass, which is very roughly 1 800 times that of the electron. Hence, most of the mass of each atom is 'concentrated' in its nucleus, which consequently has a much higher density than the atom as a whole. Experiments show that the density of a nucleus is normally about 10^{14} times the density of water. This implies that if a 5 ml teaspoonful of nuclei could be prepared, it would have a mass of about 10^{12} kg—about the mass of Ben Nevis!

In order to specify the numbers of protons and neutrons in a nucleus, two numbers are needed—its mass number and its atomic number (Figure 24). The **mass number** A of a nucleus is defined as the total number of protons and neutrons that it contains: this number gives the number of particles in the nucleus. The **atomic number** Z of the nucleus is defined as the number of protons that it contains. Hence, the number of neutrons in a nucleus is given by the difference $A - Z$ between its mass number and its atomic number (Figure 24).

ISOTOPE

Because the neutron has no electrical charge and the proton has an electrical charge of $+e$ (where e is the magnitude of the charge of the electron), the total charge of the nucleus is $+Ze$. Hence, in an atom, this nuclear charge balances the equal and opposite charge $-Ze$ of the Z electrons that orbit the nucleus (Figure 24).

You may remember from Units 11–12 that atoms whose nuclei contain the same number of protons but different numbers of neutrons have the same chemical properties. This is because these properties depend on the number of electrons in the atom, which in turn depends only on the number of protons in the nucleus.

☐ Can you remember the name given to atoms whose nuclei contain the *same* number of protons but *different* numbers of neutrons?

■ Such atoms are known as **isotopes**; their nuclei have the same atomic number Z, but have different mass numbers.

The contents of the nucleus of an element are usually noted down by writing before its chemical symbol, the mass number of the nucleus (written as a superscript) and its atomic number (written as a subscript). For example, the isotope of silicon with $A = 27$ and $Z = 14$ is written $^{27}_{14}\text{Si}$.

ITQ 7   Consider the isotope $^{68}_{30}\text{Zn}$ of the element zinc.

(a) How many protons does the nucleus contain?

(b) How many neutrons does it contain?

(c) Given that the electrical charge of the electron is approximately $-1.602 \times 10^{-19}\,\text{C}$, what is the charge of the nucleus?

(d) How many electrons move around the nucleus of a neutral atom of zinc?

(e) A nucleus X has atomic number 31. Is X an isotope of zinc?

Each element has a characteristic number of unstable isotopes (i.e. isotopes that sooner or later undergo radioactive decay) and a number of completely stable isotopes which never undergo radioactive decay. For example, magnesium has five unstable isotopes—$^{20}_{12}\text{Mg}$, $^{21}_{12}\text{Mg}$, $^{23}_{12}\text{Mg}$, $^{27}_{12}\text{Mg}$ and $^{28}_{12}\text{Mg}$—but only three stable isotopes—$^{24}_{12}\text{Mg}$, $^{25}_{12}\text{Mg}$ and $^{26}_{12}\text{Mg}$. Each stable isotope of an element occurs naturally with a characteristic relative abundance on Earth. For example, the three stable isotopes of magnesium $^{24}_{12}\text{Mg}$, $^{25}_{12}\text{Mg}$ and $^{26}_{12}\text{Mg}$ occur naturally on Earth with relative abundances of approximately 78.6%, 10.1% and 11.3%, respectively.

In Figure 25, the number of protons in each of the completely *stable* nuclei that exist in nature is plotted against the number of neutrons that they each contain. Hence, Figure 25 shows all the stable isotopes found in nature.

ITQ 8   How many completely stable isotopes are there of (a) chlorine, which has atomic number 17; (b) technetium, which has atomic number 43?

Notice from Figure 25 that *stable* isotopes whose atomic numbers are less than about 17 contain roughly the *same* number of neutrons as protons. However, stable isotopes with a greater atomic number contain *more* neutrons than protons. The reason for this phenomenon is connected with the electrical charges of the two particles. If neutrons were 'added' to a nucleus, no electrostatic force would act on them because they have no electrical charge. However, if protons were 'added' to a nucleus they would be repelled by the other protons in the nucleus, because the other protons are of course also positively charged (remember, like charges repel). Hence, it is easier to 'add' neutrons to a nucleus than it is to 'add' protons to it. You might think that it should be possible to 'add' as many neutrons as we like to a nucleus, but this turns out not to be possible in practice—if a nucleus contains too many neutrons it is unstable and undergoes radioactive decay.

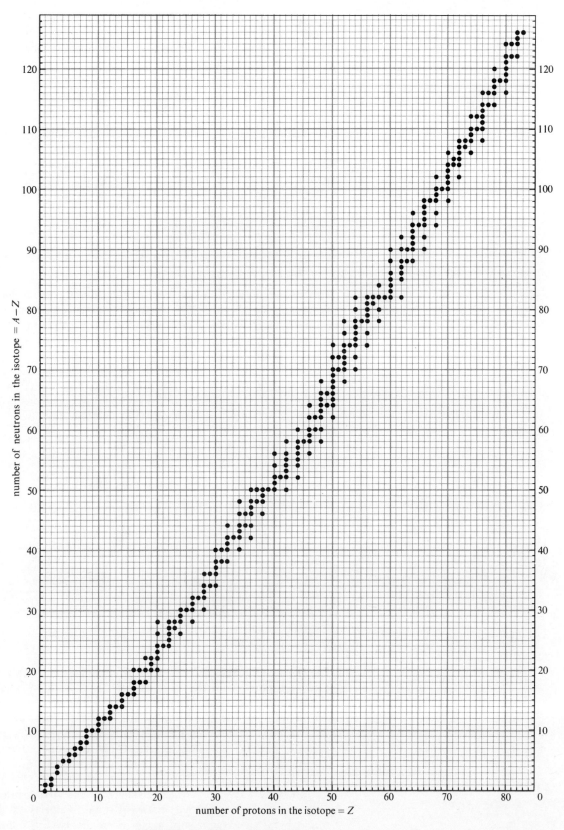

FIGURE 25   The number of protons in *completely stable* nuclei plotted against the number of neutrons that they contain.

4.2 THE STRONG INTERACTION

Why do protons and neutrons bind together to form nuclei? So far in this Course you have met three basic types of interaction that you may think could be responsible for this effect—the gravitational interaction (Unit 3), the electrostatic interaction (Unit 9) and the magnetic interaction (Units 5–6).

STRONG INTERACTION

The gravitational interaction is felt by the protons and neutrons in the nucleus but this interaction is far too weak to bind the particles together. The electrostatic interaction cannot be responsible for the binding: because neutrons have no charge, they are not bound electrostatically to each other or to the protons in the nucleus. Also, because the electrostatic force between particles with charges of the same sign is repulsive, the electrostatic force between the protons pushes them apart! It can also be shown that the magnetic interaction is not responsible for the binding.

The interaction that is responsible for the binding of the protons and neutrons in the nucleus is known as the **strong interaction**. This type of interaction has not been mentioned so far in the Course, mainly because its effects are not directly encountered in everyday life, unlike those of the much more familiar gravitational, electrostatic and magnetic interactions. The strong interaction is actually quite special in the sense that it is felt only by certain particles, for example by the proton and neutron. It is *not* felt by electrons. (We shall discuss the strong interaction in more detail in Unit 32.)

The strong interaction between protons and neutrons has four principal characteristics (Figure 26). First, it is always predominantly attractive, whether it acts between positively charged protons or between uncharged neutrons or between protons and neutrons. This is to be expected, since this interaction binds *both* types of particle to form a nucleus. The second characteristic is that the strength of the interaction is *independent* of the electrical charges and masses of the proton and neutron. This implies that the strength of the strong interaction between two neutrons is exactly the same as that between two protons and that between a neutron and a proton (all at the same separation).

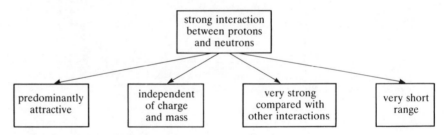

FIGURE 26   Four characteristics of the strong interaction between protons and neutrons.

The third characteristic of the strong interaction is that its strength is enormous compared with the strengths of electrostatic, magnetic and gravitational interactions. For example, the attractive strong interaction between two protons in a nucleus is very much greater than the repulsive electrostatic interaction between them—this is why they stay bound tightly in the nucleus. Finally, the strong interaction acts only over a short range, approximately 10^{-14} m. Hence, two neutrons separated by 10^{-15} m are attracted to each other by the strong interaction whereas if they were separated by, say, 10^{-12} m the strength of the strong interaction between them would be negligible. This short-range property of the strong interaction helps to explain why nuclei normally have a diameter of approximately 10^{-14} m—within this range, the protons and neutrons are tightly bound to each other by the attractive strong interaction, but outside the range the strength of the interaction is negligible.

There is an important difference between our understanding of the strong interaction and our understanding of the gravitational, magnetic and electrostatic interactions. Whereas the latter three types of interaction are described by comparatively simple laws that have been checked experimentally (e.g. the electrostatic and gravitational interactions are described in terms of Coulomb's law and Newton's gravitational law respectively), no such simple law is known for the strong interaction between protons and neutrons.

FIGURE 27   The three lowest energy levels of a $^{12}_{6}$C nucleus.

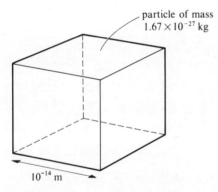

particle of mass 1.67×10^{-27} kg

10^{-14} m

FIGURE 28   A simple model of an atomic nucleus.

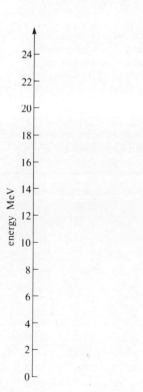

FIGURE 29   See ITQ 11.

4.3 UNDERSTANDING NUCLEAR ENERGY LEVELS (TV programme)

You saw in the Introduction that nuclei have quantized values of energy, known as energy levels (e.g. Figure 27). The spacings of the lowest energy nuclear energy levels are normally approximately a million times those of the lowest few energy levels of the electron in a hydrogen atom, so they are measured in megaelectronvolts (MeV). In this Section, we shall try to understand this by investigating the quantization of nuclear energy.

The investigation will be carried out by modelling a typical nucleus as a cubic box that contains a single particle (Figure 28). Each side of the box will be taken to be 10^{-14} m (a typical nuclear diameter) and the mass of the confined particle will be taken to be 1.67×10^{-27} kg (approximately the mass of the proton and neutron). This model has two notable virtues: it explicitly takes into account

o the size of the nucleus

o the mass of each of the particles in the nucleus.

However, the model also has several shortcomings. It is based on the somewhat unrealistic assumption that nuclei are cubic. Also, it ignores the fact that protons and neutrons have been observed experimentally to have spin. But perhaps the most potentially dangerous assumption of the model is that the details of the strong interaction between a single particle and all the other nuclear constituents are ignored. This assumption is sweeping and apparently extremely unreasonable—we shall not attempt to justify it theoretically, and shall simply go ahead and implement it and then examine the results. If the model is hopelessly unsuccessful, the assumption will obviously have to be modified.

We now want you to use the nuclear particle-in-a-box model. Try ITQs 9–11.

ITQ 9   (a) What is the quantum mechanical equation that gives the possible energy values E of a particle of mass m confined in a cubic box whose sides each have length L? (You will probably need to refer to Section 2.)

$E =$

(b) Use your answer to part (a) to complete the box below.

> Protons and neutrons in nuclei have energy levels because they are
>
> ------------------------------- .

ITQ 10   (a) Refer to the equation in the answer to part (a) of ITQ 9. Evaluate, in units of joules and to three significant figures, the quantity $h^2/(8mL^2)$ for the nuclear particle-in-a-box model (Figure 28).

(b) Using your answer to part (a) and the definition of the mégaelectronvolt MeV (1 MeV $\approx 1.602 \times 10^{-13}$ J), evaluate $h^2/(8mL^2)$ in units of MeV, to two significant figures. Enter your result in the box below.

> nuclear particle-in-a-box model
> $E = \qquad$ MeV $\times (n_1{}^2 + n_2{}^2 + n_3{}^2)$ (23)

ITQ 11   (a) Show on Figure 29 the four lowest nuclear energy levels according to the particle-in-a-box model. (Hint: refer to Figure 15).

(b) Compare the energy spacings of the lowest nuclear energy levels predicted by the particle-in-a-box model (Figure 28) with the experimentally observed nuclear energy levels for carbon shown in Figure 27. How well does the model agree with experiment?

NUCLEAR BINDING ENERGY
GRAPH

BINDING ENERGY OF A
NUCLEUS

You saw in ITQs 10 and 11 that the nuclear particle-in-a-box model successfully predicts that the lowest nuclear energy levels should be far more widely spaced in energy than those of the electron in a hydrogen atom, as predicted by the atomic particle-in-a-box model. According to this analysis, the spacings of the energy levels of the hydrogen atom and those of the typical nucleus both depend on three quantities—Planck's constant, and the size of the confining volume and the mass of the confined particle in each case. Analyses using more advanced models have confirmed this conclusion.

The two particle-in-a-box models formulated in this Unit—one of the hydrogen atom, the other of a typical nucleus—have been used with considerable success. Although the numerical predictions obtained using the two models have not been very accurate, they have nonetheless allowed qualitative answers to be given to questions Q1–Q4 (about atomic and nuclear energy levels) which were posed in the Introduction. The results we have obtained using the two models are reviewed in Table 2.

TABLE 2   Comparison between the particle-in-a-box models of the hydrogen atom and the typical nucleus

	Hydrogen atom	Typical nucleus
visualization		
model		
energy levels according to the quantum mechanical model	$E = 1.5\,\text{eV} \times (n_1{}^2 + n_2{}^2 + n_3{}^2)$	$E = 2.1\,\text{MeV} \times (n_1{}^2 + n_2{}^2 + n_3{}^2)$
questions answered qualitatively using the model	Q1 Why do atomic electrons have energy levels?	Q3 Why do protons and neutrons in nuclei have energy levels?
	A1 Because the electrons are *confined*.	A3 Because the protons and neutrons are *confined*.
		Q4 Why are the differences between the lowest energy levels of protons and neutrons in nuclei approximately a million times those of the electron in a hydrogen atom?
	Q2 Why are the differences between the lowest energy levels of the electron in a hydrogen atom a few electronvolts?	
	A2 The separations are determined to be a few electronvolts mainly by the size of the atom, by the mass of the electron, and by the value of Planck's constant.	A4 The differences in the spacing arise principally from the differences between (i) the sizes of the atom and the nucleus and (ii) the masses of the confined particles involved.

4.4 NUCLEAR BINDING ENERGIES

It is found experimentally that the minimum energy required to break up a nucleus into free protons and neutrons is normally in the range 1–2 000 MeV. Such experiments determine the **binding energy of a nucleus**, which is actually the minimum energy required to unbind the nucleus. When it is said that the 'binding energy of an oxygen nucleus $^{16}_{8}O$ is 127.6 MeV', it is meant that 127.6 MeV of energy must be transferred to an $^{16}_{8}O$ nucleus in order to break it up into eight free protons and eight free neutrons with zero kinetic energy (Figure 30).

FIGURE 30 At least 127.6 MeV of energy must be transferred to a $^{16}_{8}O$ nucleus in order to unbind completely its constituent protons and neutrons.

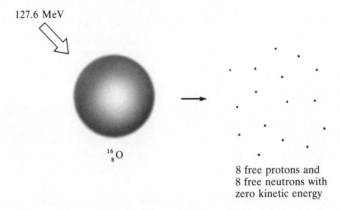

127.6 MeV

$^{16}_{8}O$

8 free protons and 8 free neutrons with zero kinetic energy

If the mass number A of a nucleus and its total binding energy are known, it is easy to calculate the average amount of energy required to unbind a *single* proton or neutron from the nucleus:

$$\begin{pmatrix}\text{average binding energy}\\\text{of a nucleus per}\\\text{constituent proton}\\\text{and neutron}\end{pmatrix}=\dfrac{\begin{pmatrix}\text{minimum energy required to unbind}\\\text{completely all the protons}\\\text{and neutrons in the nucleus}\end{pmatrix}}{\text{mass number } A \text{ of the nucleus}} \quad (24)$$

For example, consider again the oxygen $^{16}_{8}O$ nucleus, which has mass number $A = 16$ and so contains 16 particles (8 protons and 8 neutrons). Because the binding energy of an $^{16}_{8}O$ nucleus is 127.6 MeV,

$$\begin{pmatrix}\text{average binding energy of an}\\^{16}_{8}O \text{ nucleus per constituent}\\\text{proton and neutron}\end{pmatrix}=\dfrac{127.6\,\text{MeV}}{16}\approx 7.98\,\text{MeV}$$

In Figure 31, the **nuclear binding energy graph**, the average binding energy of a nucleus per constituent proton and neutron is plotted against mass number for many nuclei. You should check that the point for $^{16}_{8}O$ (calculated above) has been plotted correctly on this graph.

There are three features that you should note about Figure 31.

- The graph has a maximum around the points that correspond to $^{56}_{26}Fe$ and $^{62}_{28}Ni$, whose average binding energy per constituent proton and neutron is 8.79 MeV. The constituents of these nuclei are more tightly bound than those of any other nucleus.

- The *average* energy required to unbind a proton or neutron from any of the nuclei with mass number A greater than 10 is approximately 8 MeV.

- The amounts of energy required to unbind a proton or neutron from certain nuclei are markedly higher than those immediately closest to them in mass number—in other words, there are certain nuclei that are exceptionally strongly bound for their mass numbers. Three such nuclei are $^{16}_{8}O$, $^{12}_{6}C$, and $^{4}_{2}He$ (an α-particle).

4.5 NUCLEAR MASSES AND EINSTEIN'S EQUATION

In 1905, Einstein formulated the **special theory of relativity**, a revolutionary theory of space and time. The most important result of the theory for our purposes is that *an amount of energy (of any type) has an equivalent mass.* More specifically, Einstein predicted that the mass m that is equivalent to energy E is given by

$$m = E/c^2 \tag{25}$$

where c is the speed of light in a vacuum, approximately $3 \times 10^8 \, \mathrm{m \, s^{-1}}$. Equation 25 is better known in the form

$$E = mc^2 \tag{26}$$

which is generally known as **Einstein's equation**. The statement 'an amount of energy has an associated mass' implies that if the energy of a particle changes its mass must also change. This is correct, but it appears to lead to a problem—how can the mass of a particle be defined uniquely? The way out of this is simply to define the **rest mass** of any entity, which is the mass of the entity as measured by an observer *relative to whom the entity is at rest*. The masses of the electron, proton and neutron quoted on the back of the physics and general science Units are actually the *rest* masses of the particles. (The rest mass of the photon turns out to be zero.)

Why did hundreds of years elapse between the invention of the concept of energy and Einstein's discovery of the connection between energy and mass? Well, consider the mass that is equivalent to a joule of energy, roughly the energy required to lift an apple by 1 m on Earth: this amount of energy is, within a few orders of magnitude, typical of the energies normally encountered in everyday life. Equation 25 says that the mass that is equivalent to a joule of energy is given by

$$\text{mass equivalent to 1 J of energy} = \frac{1 \, \mathrm{J}}{(3 \times 10^8 \, \mathrm{m \, s^{-1}})^2}$$

$$\approx 10^{-17} \, \mathrm{kg}$$

i.e. $0.000\,000\,000\,000\,000\,01$ kg, much too small to be measured using conventional weighing instruments! In view of this, it is hardly surprising that the connection between energy and mass was not discovered in everyday experiments—it took the genius of Einstein for the connection to be *predicted*.

For more than twenty years after Einstein proposed his equation, it could not be checked, mainly because the energies involved in chemical reactions are associated with masses that are much too small to be observed. However, in the 1930s, when it became possible to study nuclear reactions, the validity of Einstein's equation was clearly demonstrated. In order to understand why the consequences of the equation are comparatively easy to observe in the case of nuclei, think again about the example illustrated in Figure 30, which shows an oxygen nucleus $^{16}_{8}\mathrm{O}$ that is broken up into its free constituents when 127.6 MeV of energy have been transferred to it. Remember that 127.6 MeV is the *minimum* energy required to unbind the nucleus, so after this energy has been transferred the unbound constituents have zero kinetic energy.

The situation shown in Figure 30 can be expressed by writing down a kind of energy equation

$$^{16}_{8}\mathrm{O} \text{ nucleus} + 127.6 \, \mathrm{MeV} \longrightarrow \begin{array}{l} \text{8 free protons and 8 free neutrons} \\ \text{with zero kinetic energy} \end{array}$$

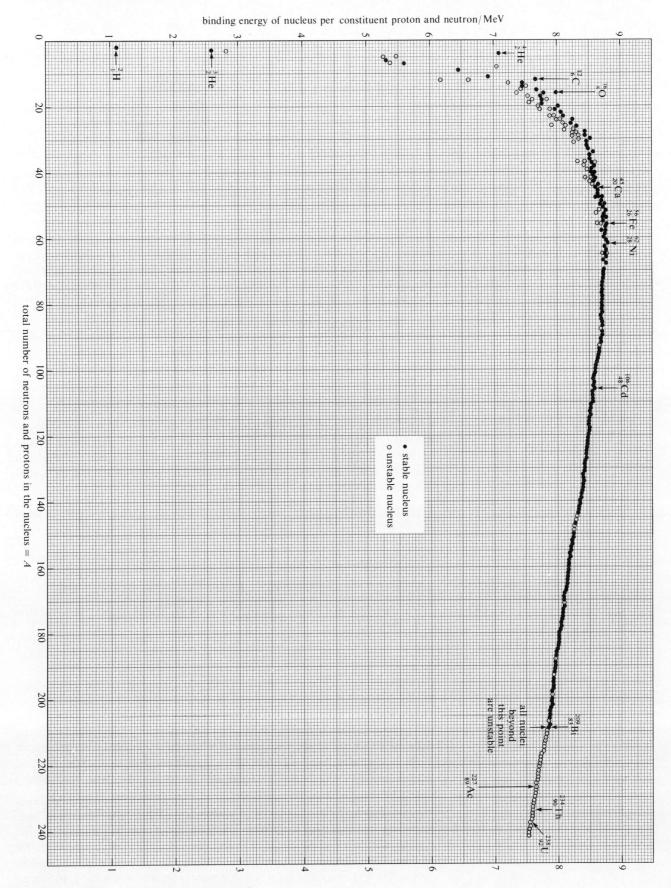

FIGURE 31   The nuclear binding energy graph.

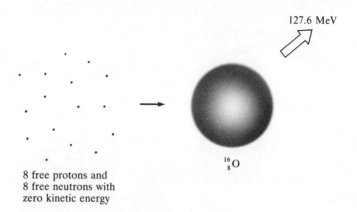

FIGURE 32   When 8 free protons and 8 free neutrons with zero kinetic energy coalesce to form a $^{16}_{8}$O nucleus, 127.6 MeV of energy are released (cf. Figure 30).

This 'equation' also implies that if the reverse process were to occur (Figure 32), i.e. if the 8 free protons and 8 free neutrons with zero kinetic energy were to coalesce to form the $^{16}_{8}$O nucleus, then 127.6 MeV of energy would be released (electromagnetic radiation would be emitted with this energy). In order to see this, it is best to write the 'equation' the other way round:

8 free protons and 8 free neutrons with zero kinetic energy $\longrightarrow$ $^{16}_{8}$O nucleus + 127.6 MeV

This implies that

total rest mass of 8 free protons and 8 free neutrons $=$ rest mass of $^{16}_{8}$O nucleus $+$ mass equivalent to 127.6 MeV

which in turn implies that *the sum of the rest masses of the free protons and neutrons is greater than the rest mass of the nucleus that is formed from them.* How much less than the sum of the rest masses of the free protons and neutrons is the rest mass of the nucleus? Let us calculate the difference using Einstein's equation.

We know the energy released in units of MeV so, in order to calculate the energy's equivalent mass in SI units of kilograms we must first convert the energy into SI units of joules. Because 1 MeV $\approx 1.602 \times 10^{-13}$ J,

$$127.6 \, \text{MeV} = 127.6 \, \text{MeV} \times (1.602 \times 10^{-13} \, \text{J MeV}^{-1})$$

$$= 2.044 \times 10^{-11} \, \text{J}$$

Hence, using Equation 25 and the value of the speed of light in a vacuum ($c \approx 2.998 \times 10^{8} \, \text{m s}^{-1}$),

$$\text{mass equivalent to } 127.6 \, \text{MeV} = \frac{2.044 \times 10^{-11} \, \text{J}}{(2.998 \times 10^{8} \, \text{m s}^{-1})^2}$$

$$= 2.27 \times 10^{-28} \, \text{kg}$$

Hence, the mass that is equivalent to the energy released is tiny—the sum of the rest masses of the free protons and neutrons is only very slightly greater than the rest mass of the nucleus that is formed from them. But the crucial point is that this mass difference is a significant and *measurable* fraction (approximately 0.8%) of the total rest mass of the free constituents (approximately 2.68×10^{-26} kg).

Experiments have confirmed this prediction of Einstein's equation and, moreover, the principle used in this discussion of the $^{16}_{8}$O nucleus applies equally well to all other nuclei that contain more than one constituent: *the rest mass of a nucleus that contains more than one constituent is less than the sum of the rest masses of its free constituents, because when the constituents coalesced to form the nucleus, energy was released.* This applies not only to nuclei—it applies to *any* group of particles that are bound together. For example, a hydrogen chloride molecule HCl, which consists of a hydrogen atom H bound to a chlorine atom Cl, has a rest mass that is *less* than the sum of the rest masses of a free hydrogen atom and a free chlorine atom. The mass difference is, however, only approximately three hundredths of a millionth of a per cent of the rest mass of the molecule—far too small to be measured using conventional weighing apparatus.

This illustrates the general point that the difference between the rest mass of a bound system and the sum of the rest masses of its free constituents is always proportionately much larger for nuclei than it is for molecules (and atoms). This is why Einstein's equation is much more important in nuclear physics than it is in chemistry.

SUMMARY OF SECTION 4

1   Each atom has a nucleus—a positively charged 'core' that has a 'diameter' of approximately 10^{-14} m. Apart from the hydrogen nucleus ${}^1_1$H, which is a proton, nuclei in general consist of combinations of protons and neutrons.

2   Each nucleus is characterized by its atomic number Z (which specifies the number of protons it contains) and its mass number A (which specifies the total number of its constituent protons and neutrons). Different isotopes of an element are characterized by different mass numbers but the same atomic number.

3   Each type of nucleus has only a certain number of unstable isotopes (which sooner or later undergo radioactive decay) and a certain number of completely stable isotopes (which never undergo radioactive decay). There are a finite number of completely stable nuclei (Figure 25).

4   Protons and neutrons in nuclei are bound together by the strong interaction, whose four principal characteristics are given in Figure 26.

5   A particle-in-a-box model can be used to understand why nuclei have energy levels and why the energy spacings of the lowest of these levels are approximately a million times the energy spacings of the lowest energy levels of the electron in a hydrogen atom.

6   The binding energy graph (Figure 31) shows that the average binding energy of a nucleus per constituent proton and neutron is approximately 8 MeV for most nuclei.

7   The special theory of relativity tells us that an amount of energy has an equivalent mass. The mass m that is equivalent to energy E is given by Einstein's equation $E = mc^2$, where c is the speed of light in a vacuum. The equation leads to an understanding of why the rest mass of each nucleus that contains more than one constituent particle is *less* than the sum of the rest masses of its free constituents.

SAQ 5   Which two of the following statements about the interactions between particles in a nucleus are correct?

(a) Protons and neutrons in the nucleus are not subject to a gravitational interaction.

(b) The particles in a nucleus are bound together by the strong interaction.

(c) The magnitude of the strong interaction between two neutrons separated by 10^{-16} m is less than the magnitude of the strong interaction between two protons at the same separation.

(d) The magnitude of the strong interaction between two neutrons that are separated by 1 cm is negligible.

SAQ 6   (a) The principal interactions that are felt by protons in a nucleus are strong and electrostatic. Are these interactions respectively attractive or repulsive?

(b) Figure 25 indicates that after a certain atomic number ($Z = 83$) no nuclei are completely stable. Use your answer to part (a) to suggest why. (Hint: think about the interactions of the constituent protons.)

SAQ 7 The minimum energy required to break apart the stable beryllium nucleus $^{10}_{4}\text{Be}$ into free protons and neutrons is approximately 64.98 MeV.

(a) What is the average binding energy of the $^{10}_{4}\text{Be}$ nucleus per constituent proton and neutron? Mark the value on the nuclear binding energy graph (Figure 31.)

(b) Are the constituents of a $^{10}_{4}\text{Be}$ nucleus more or less tightly bound than those of a $^{12}_{6}\text{C}$ nucleus?

SAQ 8 Refer to Figure 31.

(a) What is the *minimum* energy required to unbind the constituents of a $^{4}_{2}\text{He}$ nucleus (i.e. an α-particle)?

(b) How much energy is released when an α-particle is produced from two free protons and two free neutrons?

(c) What is the difference between the rest mass of an α-particle and the sum of the rest masses of two free protons and two free neutrons?

5 RADIOACTIVE DECAYS OF NUCLEI

You saw in the previous Section that only certain nuclei are completely stable (Figure 25), and that there are many unstable nuclei, which sooner or later undergo **radioactive decay**. This Section concerns types of radioactive decay that can occur, and we shall also discuss briefly why the products of radioactive decay can be dangerous to life. (We shall not be discussing the half-lives of the radioactive nuclei, as that subject was considered in detail earlier in the Course, notably in Units 11–12 and 28–29.)

You have met the phenomenon of radioactivity several times in this Course. We mentioned it in Units 7–8 and 27, where you saw that the energy released in radioactive decays is mainly responsible for the very high temperatures of the Earth's interior and, ultimately, for the energy that drives the massive lithospheric plates in the plate tectonic process. You also saw in Units 11–12 how the ages of objects such as biblical documents can be estimated by measuring the amount of $^{14}_{6}\text{C}$ that they contain—this is known as carbon dating. Finally, you saw in Units 28–29 how the ages of certain minerals can be determined from a knowledge of the decay rates of their radioactive constituents.

5.1 α-DECAY

When a nucleus undergoes **α-decay**, a helium nucleus $^{4}_{2}\text{He}$ (α-particle) is ejected and another nucleus is formed. The mass number of the other nucleus is four less and its atomic number is two less than the corresponding values of the original nucleus. An example of α-decay is provided by the decay of a stationary nucleus of $^{238}_{92}\text{U}$ (Figure 33):

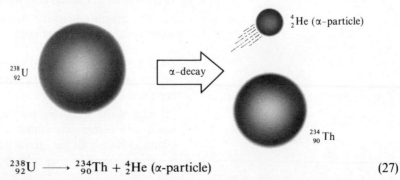

FIGURE 33 Schematic visualization of the α-decay of a $^{238}_{92}\text{U}$ nucleus.

$$^{238}_{92}\text{U} \longrightarrow {}^{234}_{90}\text{Th} + {}^{4}_{2}\text{He} \ (\alpha\text{-particle}) \tag{27}$$

It is found experimentally that the total kinetic energy of the products is approximately 4.3 MeV, nearly all of which is carried by the α-particle—in other words, the energy released in the reaction is approximately 4.3 MeV. (We say that energy is released in a reaction when the total kinetic energy of the particles before the reaction is less than the kinetic energy afterwards.) The rest mass of the uranium nucleus must therefore be greater than the sum of the rest masses of the thorium and helium nuclei. Using the law of conservation of energy, and assuming that the uranium nucleus decays from rest,

$$\begin{array}{l} \text{energy equivalent} \\ \text{to rest mass of} \\ {}^{238}_{92}\text{U} \end{array} = \begin{array}{l} \text{energy equivalent} \\ \text{to rest mass of} \\ {}^{234}_{90}\text{Th} \end{array} + \begin{array}{l} \text{energy equivalent} \\ \text{to rest mass of} \\ {}^{4}_{2}\text{He} \end{array} + \begin{array}{l} \text{total kinetic} \\ \text{energy of} \\ {}^{234}_{90}\text{Th and } {}^{4}_{2}\text{He} \end{array} \qquad (28)$$

☐ By how much does the rest mass of the uranium nucleus exceed the sum of the rest masses of the thorium and helium nuclei?

■ Because 4.3 MeV of energy are released in the reaction, Equation 28 tells us that the energy equivalent to the rest mass of the uranium nucleus is greater than the sum of the energies due to the rest masses of the thorium nucleus and the helium nucleus by 4.3 MeV. It follows that the rest mass of the uranium nucleus is greater than the sum of the rest masses of the thorium and helium nuclei by the mass that is equivalent to 4.3 MeV:

$$\text{mass equivalent to } 4.3\,\text{MeV} = 4.3\,\text{MeV}/c^2$$

$$= 4.3\,\text{MeV} \times \frac{1.6 \times 10^{-13}\,\text{J MeV}^{-1}}{(3.0 \times 10^{8}\,\text{m s}^{-1})^2}$$

$$\approx 7.6 \times 10^{-30}\,\text{kg}$$

As you can see from Figure 34, the constituents of the thorium nucleus are more tightly bound than those of the original uranium nucleus. This always happens in α-decay—the heavy nucleus formed is always more tightly bound than was the original nucleus.

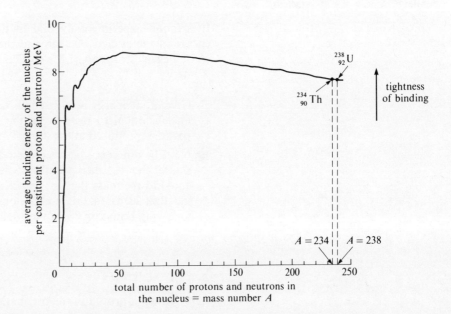

FIGURE 34   Sketch of the nuclear binding energy graph (Figure 31), with the values for the ${}^{238}_{92}\text{U}$ and ${}^{234}_{90}\text{Th}$ marked on.

5.2 β⁻-DECAY

You saw in Units 11–12 that in **β⁻-decay** a neutron in an unstable nucleus transforms into a proton with the emission of an electron. Thus, the nucleus formed after the decay contains one more proton than the original nucleus, but both nuclei contain the same total number of particles. Hence, the nucleus formed in β⁻-decay has an atomic number that is greater by one than that of the original nucleus, and both nuclei have the same mass number. An example of a nucleus that undergoes β⁻-decay is ${}^{15}_{6}\text{C}$:

$$^{15}_{6}\text{C} \longrightarrow {}^{15}_{7}\text{N} + {}^{0}_{-1}\text{e}^{-} \qquad (29)$$

β^+-DECAY

γ-DECAY

EXCITED NUCLEUS

Now it is time to admit that the account that we gave of β^--decay in Units 11–12 was incomplete. In this type of decay, a particle known as an electron antineutrino $\bar{\nu}_e$ is also emitted. This particle, which will be discussed further in Unit 32, has no electrical charge, zero atomic number and zero mass number.

Equation 29 should therefore be rewritten as

$$^{15}_6C \longrightarrow \ ^{15}_7N + \ ^{\ 0}_{-1}e^- + \bar{\nu}_e \tag{30}$$

You should now cross out Equation 29 to remind yourself that it is not correct! The process that occurs in a $^{15}_6C$ nucleus that undergoes β^--decay is the transformation of a neutron n into a proton p, an electron and an electron antineutrino $\bar{\nu}_e$. This is the basic process of β^--decay:

$$\boxed{\text{basic } \beta^-\text{-decay process} \quad n \longrightarrow p + \underbrace{e^- + \bar{\nu}_e}_{\text{ejected}}} \tag{31}$$

The β^--decay of $^{15}_6C$ (Equation 30) is illustrated schematically in Figure 35.

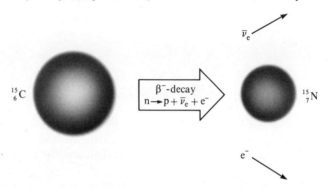

FIGURE 35   Schematic visualization of the β^--decay of a $^{15}_6C$ nucleus.

It is found experimentally that in this particular decay, the total kinetic energy of the ejected electron and the electron antineutrino is of the order of a megaelectronvolt, 1 MeV. This is typical of the energy released in β^--decay.

☐ Given that energy is released in β^--decay, is the rest mass of the original nucleus equal to the sum of the rest masses of the nucleus and other particles produced in the decay?

■ No. The difference between the rest mass of the original nucleus and the sum of the rest masses of the nucleus and the other particles produced is equal to the mass that is equivalent to the energy released. (The reasoning that leads to this conclusion is identical with the reasoning used following Equation 28, in the analogous case of α-decay.)

5.3 β^+-DECAY

In **β^+-decay**, a proton in the original nucleus transforms into a neutron and two particles that are ejected, a positron e^+ and an electron neutrino ν_e:

$$\boxed{\text{basic } \beta^+\text{-decay process} \quad p \longrightarrow n + \underbrace{e^+ + \nu_e}_{\text{ejected}}} \tag{32}$$

You have met neither the e^+ nor the ν_e particle so far in the Course but you will become more familiar with them in Unit 32. For the moment, all you need to know about them is that both have zero mass number, and that the positron has the same positive charge as that of the proton whereas the electron neutrino has no charge. These properties imply that the nucleus formed after β^+-decay has the same mass number as the original nucleus, whereas the atomic number of the nucleus formed is one less than that of the original nucleus.

An example of a nucleus that undergoes β^+-decay is $^{11}_6C$: after the decay, the stable boron nucleus $^{11}_5B$ is formed (Figure 36):

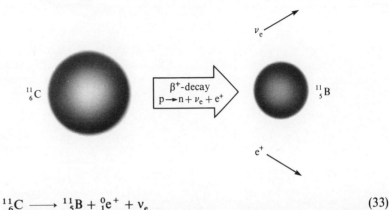

FIGURE 36 Schematic visualization of the β^+-decay of a $^{11}_6C$ nucleus.

$$^{11}_6C \longrightarrow {}^{11}_5B + {}^0_1e^+ + \nu_e \tag{33}$$

The energy released in this β^+-decay process (and in most others) is of the order of a megaelectronvolt.

5.4 γ-DECAY

The process of **γ-decay** is the simplest radioactive decay process to understand, because it is exactly analogous to the emission of a photon of electromagnetic radiation after an electron in an atom in an excited state makes a transition to a lower energy level.

The process of γ-decay usually occurs after an **excited nucleus**—a nucleus with an energy greater than its lowest possible energy— is produced in an α- or β-decay. When a proton or neutron in an excited nucleus makes a transition to a lower energy level, a photon of electromagnetic radiation is emitted with an energy equal to the difference in energy of the two levels involved.

☐ Bearing in mind what you know about the differences between the lowest energy levels of nuclei, what do you expect to be a reasonable estimate of the energy of a photon emitted from an excited nucleus?

■ Roughly of the order of *millions* of electronvolts, MeV. The energy of the photon is equal to the difference between the two energy levels involved. As you saw in Section 4, this difference is roughly of the order of megaelectronvolts.

A photon with an energy of the order of megaelectronvolts is called a γ-ray—that, of course, is why the process of γ-ray emission is called γ-decay. It would be reasonable to object that the process is not really a decay but a *transition*, so it would perhaps be better to call the process a γ-transition. However, γ-decay is the term that is used conventionally to describe the process, so we shall continue to use it here.

NUCLEAR DECAY CHAIN

NUCLEAR DECAY CHANNEL

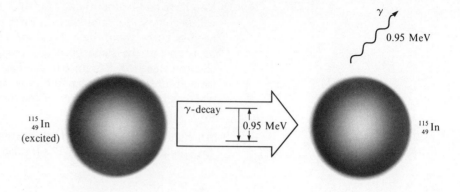

FIGURE 37 Schematic visualization of the γ-decay of an excited $^{115}_{49}$In nucleus.

An example of γ-decay is illustrated in Figure 37. In this case, a γ-ray photon is emitted with an energy of 0.95 MeV when an excited indium nucleus $^{115}_{49}$In makes a transition to an energy level that is lower by 0.95 MeV:

$$\underset{\substack{\text{excited}\\\text{nucleus}}}{^{115}_{49}\text{In}} \longrightarrow \underset{\substack{\text{ejected}\\\text{photon}}}{^{115}_{49}\text{In} + \gamma} \tag{34}$$

☐ Is the rest mass of the excited $^{115}_{49}$In nucleus, greater than, less than or equal to the rest mass of the $^{115}_{49}$In nucleus left after the γ-decay?

■ Because total energy is conserved, the energy that is equivalent to the rest mass of the excited nucleus is *greater* than the energy equivalent to the rest mass of the nucleus left after the γ-decay:

energy equivalent to the rest mass of excited $^{115}_{49}$In = energy equivalent to the rest mass of $^{115}_{49}$In left after γ-decay + 0.95 MeV energy of the photon

Hence, the difference between the rest mass of the excited $^{115}_{49}$In nucleus and the rest mass of the $^{115}_{49}$In nucleus is the mass that is equivalent to the 0.95 MeV energy (approximately 1.7×10^{-30} kg).

We ought to point out that α-, β- and γ-decays are not the only kinds of radioactivity—there are other ways in which nuclei can spontaneously decay. For example, in 1984 two physicists at Oxford University discovered a new (and very rare) type in which the radium nucleus $^{223}_{88}$Ra decays into a lead nucleus $^{209}_{82}$Pb with the ejection of a $^{14}_{6}$C nucleus! Also, as you will see in Section 6, there is a process called spontaneous nuclear fission, which should also be classified as a type of radioactive decay.

5.5 DECAY CHAINS

Most unstable nuclei do *not* decay in one step: the majority of them decay via several steps before a completely stable one is formed. For example, consider the decay $^{238}_{92}$U → $^{206}_{82}$Pb, which you met in connection with geological dating in Units 28–29. After the decay, the mass number of the original nucleus has decreased by 32 and its atomic number has decreased by 10. Clearly, the uranium nucleus has not undergone just one α-, β^-- or β^+-decay; the nucleus has undergone several decays in what is usually called a **nuclear decay chain**. You can trace for yourself the 'links' in the chain using Figure 38.

The Figure shows that the $^{238}_{92}$U nucleus first undergoes α-decay to form the nucleus $^{234}_{90}$Th, which then undergoes β^--decay to form a $^{234}_{91}$Pa nucleus. And so the decays go on until, finally, the completely stable lead nucleus $^{206}_{82}$Pb is formed. One interesting point about the decay chain shown in Figure 38 is that when the nucleus $^{214}_{83}$Bi is formed, it can undergo *either* α-decay to form $^{210}_{81}$Tl *or* β^--decay to form $^{214}_{84}$Po—the $^{214}_{83}$Bi nucleus is said to have two **nuclear decay channels**.

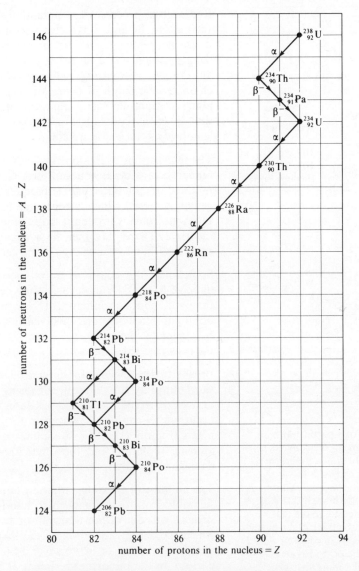

FIGURE 38   The decay chain $^{238}_{92}$U $\longrightarrow$ $^{206}_{82}$Pb.

5.6 HAZARDS OF RADIOACTIVITY

Most people are aware that the products of radioactive processes can be hazardous. The after-effects of the dropping of the nuclear bombs on Japan in 1945 and of the more recent tragedy at Chernobyl (Figure 39) chillingly bear witness to the possible dangers. But *why* are the products of radioactive processes potentially hazardous to living organisms? And to what extent are these products dangerous in everyday life? We shall discuss these questions briefly in this Section.

FIGURE 39   On 26 April 1986, at 01.23 a.m., one of the plants at the Chernobyl nuclear power station exploded when the nuclear reactions in the plant went out of control. At the subsequent enquiry, it was found that the accident was due to the failure of the engineers at the plant to observe standard safety procedures.

IONIZING RADIATION

TABLE 3 Ranges of some types of ionizing radiation

Type of ionizing radiation	Range in tissue
α-particles	10^{-5} to 10^{-4} m
β-particles	10^{-3} to 10^{-2} m
γ- and X-rays	through body

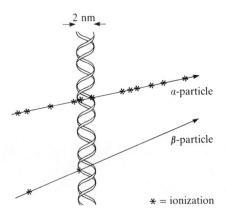

← 2 nm →

α-particle

β-particle

* = ionization

FIGURE 40 An α-particle with an energy of a few megaelectronvolts is much more likely than a β-particle to damage both strands of a DNA molecule. In each single ionization shown here, approximately 33 eV of energy are transferred. (Note that we have not shown the track of a γ-particle on this Figure as no ionizations would occur on the scale of the Figure: γ-radiation is even more sparsely ionizing than β-particles.)

Radioactive processes are potentially dangerous because their products—such as α-, β- and γ-particles—normally have sufficient kinetic energy to ionize matter (in particular, living tissue) with harmful effects. These ionizing products—and all other particles that can ionize matter—are generally known as **ionizing radiation**, and each type of this radiation has a characteristic depth of penetration into tissue (Table 3). Also, each type of ionizing radiation has a characteristic ionization density for living tissue, that is, each type causes a characteristic number of ionizations per unit length of its track (Figure 40).

The interactions of the ionizing radiation with water are very important for human beings because about 80% of the body is water. The ions produced in these interactions can subsequently damage molecules of DNA, the genetic material which is contained inside the nuclei of the body's cells. If a DNA molecule is broken it may rejoin, but the repair may be incomplete or incorrect. There may then be a change in the structure of the DNA molecule and therefore a change in the genetic message.

Sometimes, the death of a cell occurs as a result of radiation-induced damage to a DNA molecule in the cell's nucleus. However, surviving cells that still contain damaged DNA may become transformed. If damage occurs at gene locations involved in cell regulation, then cancer can result. In a gamete, the breaking of the DNA may lead to inherited disorders in the organism's descendants.

Breaks in the DNA strands can result in chromosome structural aberrations that may activate cancer-causing genes (oncogenes). These aberrations may be observed during mitosis soon after the initial radiation damage has occurred, when they may appear, for example, as misjoined breaks or fragments (Figure 41). Table 4 summarizes the observable biological effects of ionizing radiation and the times at which they occur after the radiation damage originally took place.

The amount of ionizing radiation required to kill an organism varies considerably from one organism to another. Most mammals, including *Homo sapiens*, will die within a month or two of receiving a dose of radiation in which the energy absorbed by the tissue is roughly $10\,\mathrm{J\,kg^{-1}}$. Most insects can survive doses of up to several hundred joules per kilogram. For comparison, in the biology experiment at Summer School, the irradiated wheat seedlings were exposed to a radiation dose of about $5\,000\,\mathrm{J\,kg^{-1}}$!

It is worth noting that the effects of a dose of ionizing radiation on an organism depend on the time over which the dose is delivered. For example, for someone who receives a dose of $5\,\mathrm{J\,kg^{-1}}$ in a few minutes, there is a chance of roughly 50% of death within two months from damage to the

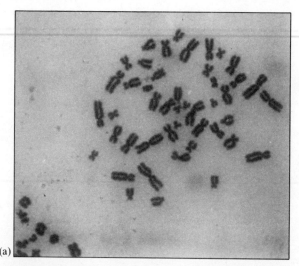
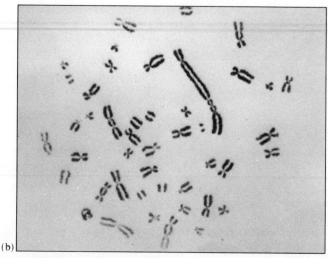

(a)   (b)

FIGURE 41 The biological effects of radiation. Both pictures show chromosome preparations from white blood cells of a human male. (a) Chromosomes from unirradiated blood, in which the chromatids of each pair are attached to each other only at the centromere. (b) In chromosomes from irradiated blood, abnormal structures can be seen. These result from the repair of damaged molecules being incomplete or incorrect. (Photos courtesy of (a) Berkeley Nuclear Laboratories and (b) National Radiological Protection Board.)

TABLE 4 Some ionizing radiation effects in mammals and the timescale over which the effects occur

Biological level or event	Important effects of ionizing radiation	Timescale
ionization	production of radicals (i.e. reactive molecules) and excited molecules	10^{-14} to 10^{-3} seconds
molecular	damage to macromolecules (e.g. enzymes, RNA and DNA); interference with metabolic pathways	seconds to hours
subcellular	damage to cell membranes, nucleus, chromosomes, mitochondria etc.	seconds to days
cellular	inhibition of cell division; cell transformation; cell death	minutes to years
tissue and organ	disruption of central nervous system; cell death in the gastro-intestinal tract and in bone marrow; cancer induction	minutes to decades
animal	death or life-shortening	minutes to decades
animal populations	genetic changes due to gene and chromosome mutations in individuals	months to generations

bone marrow. However, if the same dose is delivered over several years, the chance of death is roughly 10%, and in this case death would result from long-term effects, such as cancer.

You may well be wondering what dose of ionizing radiation you receive from day to day. The *average* annual dose for people living in the United Kingdom is approximately $2.2 \times 10^{-3} \, \mathrm{J\,kg^{-1}}$, and this dose is the result of contributions from several sources, as you can see in Figure 42. This Figure shows that by far the greatest contribution to the total average dose comes from natural background sources (which correspond to the shaded part of the Figure). These sources include cosmic rays from outer space (Unit 32), and the radioactive processes that occur within the Earth and in surface rocks and soil. In addition, we are all exposed to ionizing radiation from natural and artificial radioactive nuclei that enter our bodies through the food we eat and the air we breathe. Some of these nuclei are potentially more harmful than others if they are concentrated or retained in tissues that are particularly sensitive to the effects of radiation, for example the bone marrow and the lungs. In the UK, probably the most important single cause of lung cancer is (apart from smoking) radon gas, which is produced from the decay of uranium in rocks and soil.

It is worth stressing that Figure 42 applies to the *average* annual dose for people living in the UK. For someone who works with artificial sources of ionizing radiation, the ratio of artificial to natural background radiation is likely to be substantially higher than it is in the average case. For example, the average occupational dose received by workers in nuclear power stations in the UK in recent years has been about 65% of the natural background dose.

It is asserted in some quarters that the artificial background is dangerously high for many people and that the risks associated with unnatural ionizing radiation sources are unacceptable. On the other hand, it can be argued that the risks are not significantly greater than those associated with other aspects of modern life, for example, with road travel. The risks associated with ionizing radiation are extremely difficult to quantify, and they are regularly reviewed by bodies such as the International Commission on Radiological Protection (ICRP).

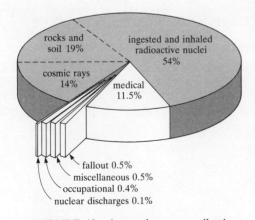

FIGURE 42 Approximate contributions to the dose of ionizing radiation received *on average* by people living in the UK. (Source: National Radiological Protection Board, 1984).

NUCLEAR FISSION

SPONTANEOUS NUCLEAR FISSION

SUMMARY OF SECTION 5

1   In the process of α-decay, a nucleus decays to form a lighter nucleus with the emission of an α-particle ($^4_2$He nucleus).

2   In the process of β^--decay, a neutron in the original nucleus transforms into a proton, emitting an electron and an electron antineutrino.

3   In the process of β^+-decay, a proton in the original nucleus transforms into a neutron, emitting a positron and an electron neutrino.

4   In the process of γ-decay, a proton or neutron in an excited nucleus makes a transition to a lower energy level, and a γ-ray photon of electromagnetic radiation is emitted.

5   Most unstable nuclei do not decay in one step to form stable nuclei. For example, the unstable nucleus $^{238}_{92}$U decays via several intermediate unstable nuclei before the completely stable nucleus $^{206}_{82}$Pb is formed (Figure 38).

6   Ionizing radiation can be hazardous to living organisms. For the majority of people living in the UK, the largest component of their total ionizing radiation dose is from natural background sources. However, for some groups of the population, the ratio of artificial to natural background ionizing radiation is substantially higher than average.

SAQ 9   A stationary nucleus of polonium $^{212}_{84}$Po undergoes α-decay and one of the decay products is a nucleus of lead (Pb).

(a)   Write down the equation for this decay.

(b)   Find an expression for the total kinetic energy of the lead nucleus and the α-particle in terms of the rest masses of the nuclei involved in the reaction and the speed of light in a vacuum.

SAQ 10   The isotope of calcium that contains 17 neutrons decays to form a potassium nucleus with mass number 37 and atomic number 19. Of what type of radioactive decay process is this an example? Write down the equation that describes the decay.

SAQ 11   The process of radioactive γ-decay is analogous to the process in which visible light is emitted from certain atoms. In what way(s) are the processes similar, and in what way(s) are they different?

SAQ 12   Which one of the following statements is correct?

(a)   The term 'ionizing radiation' is synonymous with electromagnetic radiation.

(b)   When ionizing radiation damages a DNA molecule in the nucleus of a cell, the damage is always permanent.

(c)   For the majority of people living in the UK, their average annual dose of ionizing radiation is mainly due to natural background sources.

(d)   The only known effect of ionizing radiation on human beings is the induction of cancer.

6 NUCLEAR FISSION AND FUSION

In this Section, we shall consider nuclear fission and fusion, and we shall briefly discuss nuclear power.

6.1 NUCLEAR FISSION

In the previous Section, you saw that when a nucleus undergoes α-decay, an α-particle is ejected, and a new and more tightly bound nucleus is formed. Energy is released because the rest mass of the original nucleus is greater than the sum of the rest masses of the nuclei formed. There is a similar type of process, known as **nuclear fission**, in which a heavy nucleus decays into two comparatively light nuclei of roughly equal rest mass, with the release of energy.

An example of this process is provided by a possible decay channel of the nucleus of fermium $^{256}_{100}\text{Fm}$, in which it undergoes **spontaneous fission** into a xenon nucleus $^{140}_{54}\text{Xe}$, a palladium nucleus $^{112}_{46}\text{Pd}$, and four neutrons:

$$^{256}_{100}\text{Fm} \longrightarrow {}^{140}_{54}\text{Xe} + {}^{112}_{46}\text{Pd} + 4^1_0\text{n} \tag{35}$$

(Remember that the neutron has mass number $A = 1$ and atomic number $Z = 0$, so it is denoted by ^1_0n.) The nuclear binding energy graph (Figure 43) shows that the constituents of the xenon nucleus and those in the palladium nucleus that are formed after the fission process are each more tightly bound than the constituents of the original nucleus.

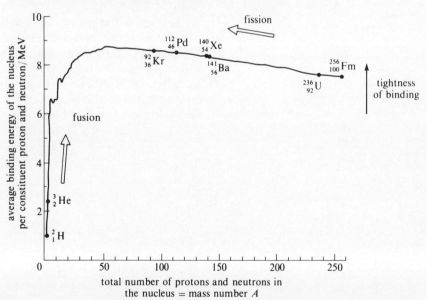

FIGURE 43 The points that correspond to the nuclei that take part in the fission and fusion reactions discussed in Section 6 shown on a sketch of the nuclear binding energy graph (Figure 31).

The rest mass of the fermium nucleus is greater than the sum of the rest masses of the products by approximately $2.67 \times 10^{-28}\,\text{kg}$, which corresponds to an energy of approximately 150 MeV. Hence, the total kinetic energy of the products is approximately 150 MeV:

$$^{256}_{100}\text{Fm} \longrightarrow \underbrace{{}^{140}_{54}\text{Xe} + {}^{112}_{46}\text{Pd} + 4^1_0\text{n}}_{\substack{\text{total kinetic} \\ \text{energy of approximately} \\ \text{150 MeV}}} \tag{36}$$

We say that the *nuclear energy* released in the reaction is approximately 150 MeV. An important point to bear in mind about this process is that the only nuclei that frequently undergo this type of decay are the heaviest, artificially produced nuclei such as $^{256}_{100}\text{Fm}$, which we have just discussed. The vast majority of nuclei much more frequently undergo the other types of spontaneous radioactive decay (α, β and γ) that we have described in Section 5.

INDUCED NUCLEAR FISSION

NUCLEAR CHAIN REACTION

NUCLEAR FUSION

A more common type of fission occurs when energy is transferred to certain heavy nuclei by bombarding them with particles, such as protons, neutrons and α-particles. An example is the fission of the uranium nucleus $^{235}_{92}$U, which hardly ever undergoes spontaneous fission but can be *induced* to undergo fission by bombarding it with neutrons*. If a $^{235}_{92}$U nucleus captures one of these neutrons, it can form an *unstable* nucleus of uranium.

☐ What are the mass number and the atomic number of the unstable nucleus formed when the uranium nucleus $^{235}_{92}$U captures a neutron?

■ The mass number of the original nucleus increases by one, so, for the nucleus formed, $A = 236$; the atomic number of the nucleus formed is the same as the original one, so $Z = 92$.

The unstable uranium nucleus $^{236}_{92}$U can decay in many different ways or, in other words, this nucleus has many decay channels. One channel through which it decays frequently is the one in which a nucleus of barium $^{141}_{56}$Ba is formed together with a nucleus of krypton $^{92}_{36}$Kr and three neutrons.

$$^{1}_{0}n + {}^{235}_{92}U \longrightarrow {}^{236}_{92}U \longrightarrow \underbrace{{}^{141}_{56}Ba + {}^{92}_{36}Kr + 3{}^{1}_{0}n} \tag{37}$$

incident   unstable   total kinetic energy
neutron   uranium   of approximately
               nucleus   200 MeV

The nuclear energy released in this **induced nuclear fission** reaction is approximately 200 MeV, which is enormous compared with the energy of the products of a typical chemical reaction. For example, the energy of the products in a single nuclear fission reaction is roughly a million times the chemical energy released in the combustion of a molecule of the octane used in the engine of a motor car.

An important feature of the fission reaction described by Equation 37 is that the neutrons that are released can be used again to bombard other $^{235}_{92}$U nuclei, which can beget yet more neutrons. As you can see from Figure 44, as more nuclei of uranium undergo fission in the **chain reaction**, so more and more energy is released in the form of kinetic energy of the products. It is in this way that the vast amounts of energy are released in the explosion of nuclear bombs.

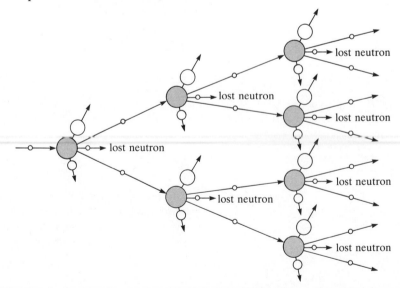

FIGURE 44 Schematic visualization of the induced fission of a $^{235}_{92}$U nucleus. If two of the released neutrons individually collide with $^{235}_{92}$U nuclei and the two $^{236}_{92}$U nuclei formed subsequently undergo fission, more energy will be released and so the process can proceed as a self-perpetuating, uncontrolled chain reaction. This is the type of reaction that underlies the working of a nuclear bomb.

* It turns out that the induced fission process is most likely to occur if the $^{235}_{92}$U nucleus is bombarded by neutrons that have a very small amount of kinetic energy (roughly 0.03 eV).

6.2 NUCLEAR FUSION

There is another type of nuclear reaction that is in a sense the opposite process to nuclear fission. In this other type of reaction, **nuclear fusion**, two light nuclei fuse to form a comparatively heavy nucleus, and energy is released.

As an example of nuclear fusion, consider the reaction in which two hydrogen nuclei ^2_1H fuse to form a nucleus of helium ^3_2He, with the emission of a neutron. In this reaction, the difference between the total rest mass of the two original hydrogen nuclei and the total rest mass of the helium nucleus and neutron produced, is such that the nuclear energy released is approximately 3.3 MeV:

$$^2_1\text{H} + \,^2_1\text{H} \longrightarrow \underbrace{^3_2\text{He} + \,^1_0\text{n}}_{\substack{\text{total kinetic} \\ \text{energy approx.} \\ \text{3.3 MeV}}} \tag{38}$$

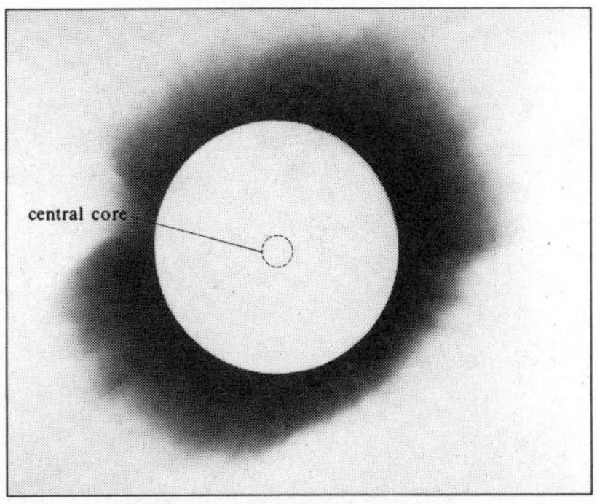

Nuclear fusion is an extremely important process. It is responsible for most of the energy we use on Earth, because a high proportion of this energy is derived from nuclear fusion reactions that take place in the Sun's central core (Figure 45). Just think, all the energy you will use in your life is derived from nuclear reactions that took place 93 million miles away!

Nuclear fusion is the process that underlies the operation of hydrogen bombs, the first of which was exploded in 1952. However, it has proved more difficult to use the process for peaceful means, as you will see in Section 6.3.

FIGURE 45 Nuclear fusion reactions take place in the Sun's central core. The energy released in these reactions fuels the planet Earth.

6.3 NUCLEAR POWER

> The energy produced by the breaking down of the atom is a very poor kind of thing. Anyone who expects a source of power from the transformation of these atoms is talking moonshine.
>
> Ernest Rutherford, addressing the British Association at Leicester on 11 September 1933.

Within ten years of Rutherford's speaking those immortal words, the world's first nuclear reactor was built (Figure 46), and by 1956 energy generated in nuclear fission reactions was being supplied to the UK's national grid. Currently, about 20% of the electrical energy produced in the United Kingdom is generated by nuclear reactors (Figure 47). Each of these reactors uses nuclear fission reactions to generate energy, and all of them use uranium as their fuel.

FIGURE 46 A sketch of the world's first nuclear reactor (because of wartime secrecy, photography was not encouraged). A self-sustaining nuclear chain reaction was first achieved on 2 December 1942 in an improvized laboratory in the squash court under the west stands of the University of Chicago's Stagg Field stadium. The leader of the team who built the reactor was the Italian physicist Enrico Fermi.

FIGURE 47 The nuclear power station at Oldbury-on-Severn in Avon. (Photo courtesy of United Kingdom Atomic Energy Authority.)

Only 0.7% of naturally occurring uranium is the ^{235}U isotope, and the remaining 99.3% is ^{238}U. This is unfortunate from the nuclear engineer's point of view because the ^{238}U isotope almost never undergoes fission—only the comparatively rare ^{235}U is useful as nuclear fuel. For this reason, reactor fuels are normally enriched artificially so that they contain a few per cent of the ^{235}U isotope.

You have already seen how enormous amounts of energy can be generated in *uncontrolled* nuclear chain reactions—this is the principle behind the nuclear bomb. In a nuclear *reactor*, the fission reaction is carefully controlled by ensuring that only *one* of the neutrons resulting from each fission event collides with a uranium nucleus (Figure 48). The kinetic energy of the products of the reactions is converted into heat, which is in turn converted into electrical energy, which is supplied to the national grid.

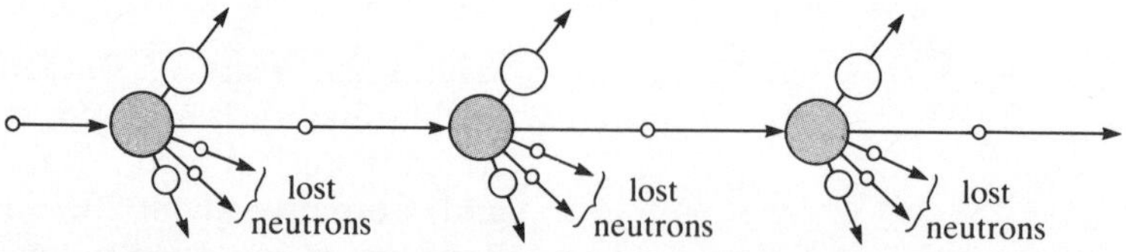

FIGURE 48 A *controlled* self-sustaining nuclear chain reaction (cf. Figure 44). This is the type of reaction that underlies the working of nuclear reactors.

The generation of electrical energy from nuclear fission reactions is of course a sensitive issue. Environmental pressure groups argue, for example, that the chances of a reactor going out of control are unacceptably high and that there are serious risks involved with the disposal of the radioactive waste products of nuclear reactions. On the other hand, proponents of nuclear power believe that the risks are acceptably low, and they point to what they believe is the low cost of nuclear energy (compared with, for example, the cost of obtaining energy from fossil fuels). These are bound to remain controversial questions for many years to come.

It is hoped that it will be possible in the future to generate electrical power using energy released in nuclear fusion reactions. Several international teams of researchers are currently investigating the feasibility of generating power from this type of nuclear reaction. This work is being done notably in the United States, the Soviet Union, Japan and Europe.

Three reactions that appear to be particularly promising as a potential source of nuclear energy are

$$^2_1H + {}^2_1H \longrightarrow {}^3_2He + {}^1_0n \tag{38}*$$

$$^2_1H + {}^2_1H \longrightarrow {}^3_1H + {}^1_1H \tag{39}$$

$$^2_1H + {}^3_1H \longrightarrow {}^4_2He + {}^1_0n \tag{40}$$

One advantage of using fusion reactions such as these to generate energy is that only Reaction 39 produces a radioactive product, ^3_1H, and that can be used up via Reaction 40. The only other source of radioactivity comes from the interactions of energetic neutrons with surrounding material. Also, the ^2_1H fuel for these reactions is available in almost unlimited quantities from the water in our lakes and oceans, and it is very cheap to extract.

These are potentially enormous advantages over the methods of generating power from nuclear fission reactions. However, there are many difficulties associated with the generation of energy from nuclear fusion. First and foremost, it is not easy to force two nuclei to fuse.

☐ Why is it difficult to make two nuclei undergo fusion?

■ Because nuclei are always positively charged, they repel each other electrostatically. In order for the nuclei to fuse, they must be propelled towards each other with sufficient energy to overcome the repulsion.

In order to initiate fusion reactions, the ingredients of the reaction must be heated to a temperature in the region of 100–200 million kelvin—considerably hotter than the central core of the Sun! So, to get the fusion reaction going, a considerable amount of energy must be transferred to the reactants. They must then be kept together at high temperature for long enough to ensure a worthwhile return of energy on the initial investment. Whereas in stars, fusing matter is held together by gravitational fields, scientists on Earth have to try to achieve this effect using magnetic fields.

It is hoped that the intensive research work being done on nuclear fusion will shortly bear fruit—optimists believe that nuclear fusion reactors may be in operation early in the 21st century. If this goal is reached, it would certainly be an enormous achievement—and one that would be of huge benefit to the human race.

SUMMARY OF SECTION 6

1 In the process of nuclear fission, the atomic nucleus that splits almost always has a large mass number, and usually splits into two smaller nuclei and a number of particles, such as neutrons.

2 In the process of nuclear fusion, two light nuclei combine to form one or more other nuclei, and possibly other particles.

3 Nuclear power stations convert energy released in nuclear fission reactions into electrical energy. It is not yet possible to harness energy released in nuclear fusion reactions, but much research is being done to investigate the feasibility of generating power from such reactions.

SAQ 13 (a) Explain briefly the difference between spontaneous nuclear fission and induced nuclear fission.

(b) A uranium nucleus $^{236}_{92}U$ spontaneously undergoes fission to form a nucleus of iron (Fe) whose *atomic* number is 26 and a nucleus of dysprosium (Dy) whose *mass* number is 180; there are no other products of the decay. Find the equation that describes this reaction.

SAQ 14 Two helium nuclei ^3_2He fuse to form *two* hydrogen nuclei ^1_1H and a nucleus of helium ^4_2He, with the release of energy.

(a) Write down the equation that describes this reaction.

(b) Is the total rest mass of the two ^3_2He nuclei equal to the sum of the rest masses of the nuclei formed in the reaction? Explain your answer briefly.

7 WHAT NEXT?

In Units 30 and 31, we have looked at the implications of two revolutionary theories of modern physics—quantum mechanics and relativity.

We have of course concentrated on quantum mechanics. You saw in Unit 30 that this theory concerns phenomena that, in some cases, transcend common sense. Before the theory was formulated, who would have thought that people are diffracted as they walk through doorways? And who would have believed that if you know for certain where something is, you can't possibly know both its speed and the direction in which it is moving? In Unit 31, you have seen that this theory allows fascinating insights into atomic and nuclear physics—in particular, the theory enables an understanding not only of why atoms and nuclei have energy levels, but also of why the differences between hydrogen's energy levels are so much smaller than the differences between the lowest energy levels of nuclei.

Einstein's special theory of relativity was needed to understand why comparatively huge amounts of energy are released in nuclear reactions, such as fission and fusion. What began in 1905 as the remarkably audacious theoretical idea that an amount of energy has an equivalent mass, is now used routinely in, for example, the design of nuclear power stations. Physicists also use the idea as an essential tool in one of the most exciting branches of modern science, particle physics. It is to this subject that we now turn, in the final Unit of the Course.

OBJECTIVES FOR UNIT 31

After you have worked through this Unit, you should be able to:

1 Explain the meaning of, and use correctly, all the terms flagged in the text.

2 Apply the formula $E_n = n^2h^2/(8ml^2)$ for the energy levels of a particle confined in one dimension between parallel plates, and explain why such a particle has energy levels. (*ITQs 1 and 2*)

3 Apply the formula $E = h^2/(8mL^2)(n_1{}^2 + n_2{}^2 + n_3{}^2)$ for the energy levels of a particle confined in a cubic box. (*ITQs 3, 5, 6 and 9–11; SAQs 1 and 2*)

4 Formulate and apply particle-in-a-box models of (i) a hydrogen atom and (ii) a typical nucleus, and recognize the limitations of the models. (*ITQs 4–6 and 9–11; SAQs 3 and 4*)

5 Recall that the lowest energy levels of the electron in a hydrogen atom are separated in energy by a few electronvolts, whereas the lowest energy levels of a typical nucleus are separated by millions of electronvolts. (*ITQs 5, 6 and 11; SAQs 3 and 4*)

6 Sketch and interpret the graph of the number of protons in completely stable nuclei plotted against the number of neutrons that they contain. (*ITQ 8; SAQ 6*)

7 Sketch and interpret the nuclear binding energy graph. (*SAQs 7 and 8*)

8 Recall the principal characteristics of the strong interaction between protons and neutrons. (*SAQs 5 and 6*)

9 Interpret and apply (in simple situations) Einstein's equation, $E = mc^2$. (*SAQs 8, 9 and 14*)

10 Recall the basic α, β^-, β^+ and γ radioactive decay processes, and explain why energy is released in each type of process. (*SAQs 9–11*)

11 Summarize, in simple terms, the hazards of ionizing radiation, and recall that for people living in the United Kingdom, the largest component of the annual average dose of ionizing radiation is due to natural background sources. (*SAQ 12*)

12 Interpret equations that describe nuclear fusion and fission, and explain why energy is released in these processes. (*SAQs 13 and 14*)

ITQ ANSWERS AND COMMENTS

ITQ 1 For each possible wavefunction of the confined particle, a whole number of half-wavelengths always 'fit' between the plates (the half-wavelengths are said to be 'quantized'). Because the particle's wavelength and the magnitude of its momentum are related, it follows that the magnitude of its momentum is quantized, and this in turn implies that its energy is quantized.

ITQ 2 (a) Using $m = 1.25 \times 10^{-27}\,kg$ and $l = 6.63 \times 10^{-5}\,m$ in conjunction with Equation 11, $E_n = n^2h^2/(8ml^2)$:

$$E_n = \frac{n^2 \times (6.63 \times 10^{-34}\,J\,s)^2}{8 \times (1.25 \times 10^{-27}\,kg) \times (6.63 \times 10^{-5}\,m)^2}$$

$$= (10^{-32}\,J) \times n^2$$

Note how the units work out:

$$(J\,s)^2/(kg\,m^2) = J^2\,s^2\,kg^{-1}\,m^{-2},$$

and because

$$1\,J = 1\,kg\,m^2\,s^{-2}$$

(Unit 9), this expression may be expanded to give

$$kg^2\,m^4\,s^{-4}\,s^2\,kg^{-1}\,m^{-2} = kg\,m^2\,s^{-2} = J.$$

(b) You should use the answer to part (a) to show the $n = 1$ energy level at $E_1 = 10^{-32}\,J$ (i.e. $10^{-32}\,J \times 1^2$) and the $n = 3$ energy level at $E_3 = 9 \times 10^{-32}\,J$ (i.e. $10^{-32}\,J \times 3^2$).

(c) The energy of the photon emitted in the transition from $n = 3$ to $n = 1$ is $8 \times 10^{-32}\,J$.

The energy $\Delta E_{3 \to 1}$ of the photon emitted in the transition is equal to the energy difference between the $n = 3$ energy level and the $n = 1$ energy level. Using the answer to part (a),

$$\Delta E_{3 \to 1} = E_3 - E_1$$
$$= [10^{-32}\,J \times 3^2] - [10^{-32}\,J \times 1^2]$$
$$= 8 \times 10^{-32}\,J$$

(d) The frequency of the emitted radiation is $1.2 \times 10^2\,Hz$ and its wavelength is $2.5 \times 10^6\,m$.

Using the standard equation for the energy E of a photon, $E = hf$, the frequency $f_{3 \to 1}$ of electromagnetic radiation emitted in the transition from $n = 3$ to $n = 1$ is

$$f_{3 \to 1} = \frac{E_3 - E_1}{h} = \frac{8 \times 10^{-32}\,J}{(6.63 \times 10^{-34}\,J\,s)}$$

$$\approx 1.2 \times 10^2\,Hz$$

(remember from Unit 10 that $1\,Hz$ is $1\,s^{-1}$). The wavelength $\lambda_{3 \to 1}$ of the radiation emitted in the transition from $n = 3$ to $n = 1$ is given by the usual equation, $c = f\lambda$, where c is the speed of light in a vacuum, $3 \times 10^8\,m\,s^{-1}$:

$$\lambda_{3 \to 1} = \frac{3 \times 10^8\,m\,s^{-1}}{1.2 \times 10^2\,Hz}$$

$$\approx 2.5 \times 10^6\,m$$

ITQ 3 (a) $E = 12h^2/(8mL^2)$. Using Equation 17,

$$E = \frac{h^2}{8mL^2}(2^2 + 2^2 + 2^2) = \frac{12h^2}{8mL^2}$$

Note that this energy level is not degenerate: it corresponds only to the wavefunction characterized by $n_1 = 2$, $n_2 = 2$ and $n_3 = 2$. Check that you have shown this level correctly on Figure 15.

(b) Yes, because this energy level corresponds to more than one wavefunction. In fact the energy level corresponds to *three* wavefunctions (Figure 15).

ITQ 4 Because the model is a very simple representation of the hydrogen atom, it is unreasonable to expect the model's predictions of the energy levels of the electron to agree exactly with the corresponding data—it is reasonable to expect only approximate agreement. If the model is to be regarded as a useful representation of the hydrogen atom, it is reasonable to assert that the model's predictions should underestimate or overestimate the corresponding data on the electron's energy values by no more than, say, one or two orders of magnitude (i.e. one or two powers of ten). In other words, if the model is to be useful, the predictions should be between 10^{-2} times and 10^2 times the experimental values. This criterion is in our opinion reasonable—you are of course at liberty to disagree!

ITQ 5 The four lowest energy levels of the particle in the box are 4.5 eV, 9 eV, 13.5 eV and 16.5 eV. *Don't forget to mark these energy levels on Figure 19!*

Figure 15 shows that the four lowest energy levels of a particle of mass m in a cubic box whose sides are each of length L are $3h^2/(8mL^2)$, $6h^2/(8mL^2)$, $9h^2/(8mL^2)$ and $11h^2/(8mL^2)$. Because in the model $h^2/(8mL^2) = 1.5\,eV$ (Equation 22), it follows that the four lowest energy levels of the particle in the atom-sized box are $3 \times 1.5\,eV = 4.5\,eV$, $6 \times 1.5\,eV = 9\,eV$, $9 \times 1.5\,eV = 13.5\,eV$ and $11 \times 1.5\,eV = 16.5\,eV$.

ITQ 6 (a) See Table 5.

(b) The agreement between the predictions of the model and the data is fairly good—the agreement is well within two powers of ten. Hence, according to the subjective criterion used in the answer to ITQ 4, the model may reasonably be regarded as a useful representation of the hydrogen atom.

TABLE 5

Transition	Energy of emitted photon
E_3 to E_2	$E_3 - E_2 = 13.5\,eV - 9\,eV = 4.5\,eV$
E_4 to E_2	$E_4 - E_2 = 16.5\,eV - 9\,eV = 7.5\,eV$
E_5 to E_2	$E_5 - E_2 = 18\,eV - 9\,eV = 9\,eV$
E_6 to E_2	$E_6 - E_2 = 21\,eV - 9\,eV = 12\,eV$

ITQ 7 (a) The nucleus contains 30 protons, because its atomic number is 30.

(b) The total number of protons and neutrons that it contains is 68 and, from (a), it contains 30 protons. It therefore contains $68 - 30 = 38$ neutrons.

(c) $+4.8 \times 10^{-18}$ C. The nucleus contains 30 protons (positively charged) and 38 neutrons, which are not charged. Since the *magnitude* of the charge of the proton is the same as that of the electron, the total charge Q of the nucleus is:

$$Q = +30 \times (1.602 \times 10^{-19} \, \text{C})$$
$$\approx +4.8 \times 10^{-18} \, \text{C}$$

(d) 30. Because the atom is neutral and the magnitude of the charge of the proton is the same as that of the electron, the number of protons N_p in the nucleus must be the same as the number of electrons N_e that move around the nucleus. Since $N_p = 30$ from (a), $N_e = 30$ also.

(e) No. All isotopes of an element have the same atomic number. So because the atomic number of $^{68}_{30}\text{Zn}$ (which is 30) differs from that of X (which is 31), X cannot be an isotope of zinc.

ITQ 8 (a) Two, because there are two points on Figure 25 that correspond to $Z = 17$. The locations of these points on the Figure tell us that the stable isotopes of chlorine contain 18 and 20 neutrons, respectively.

(b) Because there is no point corresponding to $Z = 43$, there are *no* completely stable isotopes of technetium!

ITQ 9 (a)

$$E = \frac{h^2}{8mL^2}(n_1{}^2 + n_2{}^2 + n_3{}^2) \qquad (17)*$$

where n_1, n_2 and n_3 are each equal to any whole number, i.e. 1 or 2 or 3 ... etc.

(b) Protons and neutrons in nuclei have energy levels because they are *confined*. Equation 17 shows that the energy of a particle in a cubic box is quantized, i.e. the

particle has energy levels. Hence, just as the model (in conjunction with Equation 17) was used to infer that hydrogen has energy levels because it contains a confined electron, so it is reasonable to use the model to assert that the nuclei have energy levels because they consist of confined particles (protons and neutrons).

ITQ 10 (a) $h^2/(8mL^2) = 3.29 \times 10^{-13}$ J.

The value of Planck's constant h is 6.63×10^{-34} J s, and, according to the model, $m = 1.67 \times 10^{-27}$ kg, $L = 1.00 \times 10^{-14}$ m, so

$$\frac{h^2}{8mL^2} = \frac{(6.63 \times 10^{-34} \, \text{J s})^2}{8 \times (1.67 \times 10^{-27} \, \text{kg}) \times (1.00 \times 10^{-14} \, \text{m})^2}$$
$$= 3.29 \times 10^{-13} \, \text{J}$$

(b) Because 1 MeV $\approx 1.602 \times 10^{-13}$ J,

$$\frac{h^2}{8mL^2} = \frac{3.29 \times 10^{-13} \, \text{J}}{1.602 \times 10^{-13} \, \text{J MeV}^{-1}} \approx 2.1 \, \text{MeV}$$

Hence, you should have completed Equation 23 as

$$E = 2.1 \, \text{MeV} \times (n_1{}^2 + n_2{}^2 + n_3{}^2)$$

ITQ 11 (a) The four lowest energy levels are 6.3 MeV, 12.6 MeV, 18.9 MeV and 23.1 MeV. Figure 15 shows that the four lowest energy levels of a particle of mass m in a cubic box whose sides each have length L are $3h^2/(8mL^2)$, $6h^2/(8mL^2)$, $9h^2/(8mL^2)$ and $11h^2/(8mL^2)$. Because, in the nuclear particle-in-a-box model, $h^2/(8mL^2) = 2.1$ MeV, it follows that the four lowest energy levels of the particle of mass 1.67×10^{-27} kg in the nucleus-sized cubic box are 3×2.1 MeV $= 6.3$ MeV, 6×2.1 MeV $= 12.6$ MeV, 9×2.1 MeV $= 18.9$ MeV and 11×2.1 MeV $= 23.1$ MeV. (This question is very similar to ITQ 5, which concerned a particle of mass 9.11×10^{-31} kg in an *atom*-sized cubic box.)

(b) The energy spacings agree quite well with the experimentally determined spacings of carbon's nuclear energy levels shown in Figure 27: the agreement is well within our criterion of two orders of magnitude (ITQ 4). Comparisons of the model's prediction with the lowest energy levels of other nuclei are also successful.

SAQ ANSWERS AND COMMENTS

SAQ 1 (a) Using Equation 17 with the values $h = 6.63 \times 10^{-34}$ J s, $m = 1.25 \times 10^{-28}$ kg and $L = 6.63 \times 10^{-6}$ m,

$$E = \frac{(6.63 \times 10^{-34} \, \text{J s})^2}{8 \times (1.25 \times 10^{-28} \, \text{kg}) \times (6.63 \times 10^{-6} \, \text{m})^2}$$
$$\times (n_1{}^2 + n_2{}^2 + n_3{}^2)$$

i.e. $E = (10^{-29} \, \text{J}) \times (n_1{}^2 + n_2{}^2 + n_3{}^2)$

(b) The particle's four lowest energy levels are 3×10^{-29} J, 6×10^{-29} J, 9×10^{-29} J and 11×10^{-29} J. According to Figure 15, the four lowest energy levels of a particle of mass m in a cubic box whose sides are each of length L are $3h^2/(8mL^2)$, $6h^2/(8mL^2)$, $9h^2/(8mL^2)$ and $11h^2/(8mL^2)$. Because $h^2/(8mL^2) = 10^{-29}$ J (as you saw in

part (a)) for the situation described in the question, it follows that the particle's four lowest energy levels are 3×10^{-29} J, 6×10^{-29} J, 9×10^{-29} J and 11×10^{-29} J.

SAQ 2 (a) 5×10^{-29} J. The energy of the photon is equal to the energy difference between the energy levels involved, i.e.

$$11 \times 10^{-29} \, \text{J} - 6 \times 10^{-29} \, \text{J} = 5 \times 10^{-29} \, \text{J}.$$

(b) 7.5×10^4 Hz. The energy of a photon is given by the standard equation $E = hf$, so the frequency f the radiation emitted in the transition specified in the question is given by the energy of the photon divided by Planck's constant.

Using the answer to part (a),

$$f = \frac{5.00 \times 10^{-29}\,\text{J}}{6.63 \times 10^{-34}\,\text{J s}} \approx 7.5 \times 10^4\,\text{Hz}$$

(c) 4×10^3 m. The wavelength λ and frequency f of electromagnetic radiation are related by the standard equation $f\lambda = c$, where c is the speed of light in a vacuum, $3 \times 10^8\,\text{m s}^{-1}$, i.e.

$$\lambda = \frac{3.0 \times 10^8\,\text{m s}^{-1}}{7.5 \times 10^4\,\text{Hz}}$$

$$\approx 4 \times 10^3\,\text{m}$$

using the answer to part (b).

SAQ 3 (a) The model was formulated in order to derive insight into the energy levels of the electron in the hydrogen atom. A more complete description of the hydrogen atom was not used, simply because that would have been too difficult—the model was extremely convenient because the expression for the energy levels of a particle in a cubic box was known at the outset (Equation 17).

(b) No—we proceeded with the simplifying assumption that the hydrogen atom is cubic in the hope that the assumption would not render the model useless. The success of the model justified our use of the assumption—this is certainly *not* to say that the success of the model proved that hydrogen atoms are cubic! It is better to say that the model's success in accounting for the energy levels of the electron in the hydrogen atom implies that the details of the atom's shape are not crucial to an understanding of its energy levels.

(c) No—as we said in the answer to ITQ 4, it is reasonable to expect the crude model to give only approximate agreement with experiment.

SAQ 4 First, the electron in the hydrogen atom has energy levels because it is *confined*. Second, the differences between the electron's lowest energy levels are determined principally by the mass of the electron, by the size of the atom and by the value of Planck's constant.

SAQ 5 Statements (b) and (d) are correct. Statement (a) is false because *all* particles are subject to a gravitational interaction; statement (b) is correct—the strong interaction is the interaction that binds together protons and neutrons in nuclei; statement (c) is false because the magnitude of the strong interaction between two neutrons at a given separation is the same as that of the strong interaction between two protons (and that between a proton and a neutron) at the same separation; statement (d) is correct because the strong interaction has a range of only about 10^{-14} m, far less than 1 cm (10^{-2} m).

SAQ 6 (a) The strong interaction between protons is attractive, whereas the electrostatic interaction between them is repulsive (because they have electrical charges of the same sign).

(b) For nuclei that have an atomic number greater than 83, the *repulsive* electrostatic interaction between their constituent protons is sufficient to overcome the *attractive* strong interaction that binds the protons and neutrons together. Hence, these nuclei are not completely stable.

SAQ 7 (a) The average binding energy of the $^{10}_{4}\text{Be}$ nucleus per constituent proton and neutron is 6.498 MeV. This is the *total* binding energy of the $^{10}_{4}\text{Be}$ nucleus (64.98 MeV) divided by the mass number of the nucleus (10). Remember, the mass number gives the total number of protons and neutrons that the nucleus contains.

(b) The constituents of the $^{10}_{4}\text{Be}$ nucleus are less tightly bound than those of the $^{12}_{6}\text{C}$ nucleus because the former nucleus has the smaller binding energy per constituent proton and neutron (Figure 31).

SAQ 8 (a) Approximately 28.4 MeV. According to Figure 31, the binding energy of a $^{4}_{2}\text{He}$ nucleus per constituent proton and neutron is approximately 7.1 MeV. Because the $^{4}_{2}\text{He}$ nucleus contains a total of *four* protons and neutrons, the total energy required to unbind a $^{4}_{2}\text{He}$ nucleus is approximately $(7.1\,\text{MeV}) \times 4 = 28.4\,\text{MeV}$.

(b) Approximately 28.4 MeV of energy are released—the amount of energy released when a nucleus is formed is equal to the minimum energy required to unbind the constituents of the nucleus.

(c) Approximately 5×10^{-29} kg. The amount of energy released when a $^{4}_{2}\text{He}$ nucleus is formed from its free constituents is approximately 28.4 MeV (part (b)), so Einstein's equation $E = mc^2$ implies that the mass that is equivalent to the energy released is

$$\frac{\text{mass equivalent to}}{28.4\,\text{MeV of energy}} = \frac{28.4\,\text{MeV}}{c^2}$$

Because $1\,\text{MeV} \approx 1.60 \times 10^{-13}$ J and $c \approx 3.00 \times 10^8$ m s^{-1},

$$\frac{\text{mass equivalent to}}{28.4\,\text{MeV of energy}} = \frac{28.4 \times (1.60 \times 10^{-13}\,\text{J})}{(3.00 \times 10^8\,\text{m s}^{-1})^2}$$

$$\approx 5 \times 10^{-29}\,\text{kg}$$

SAQ 9 (a) The equation that describes the decay is

$$^{212}_{84}\text{Po} \longrightarrow \,^{208}_{82}\text{Pb} + \,^{4}_{2}\text{He} \;(\alpha\text{-particle})$$

(b)
$$\begin{array}{l}\text{kinetic energy} \\ \text{of nuclei formed}\end{array}$$

$$= \left(\begin{array}{l}\text{rest mass} \\ \text{of } ^{212}_{84}\text{Po}\end{array} - \begin{array}{l}\text{rest mass} \\ \text{of } ^{208}_{82}\text{Pb}\end{array} - \begin{array}{l}\text{rest mass} \\ \text{of } ^{4}_{2}\text{He}\end{array} \right) \times c^2$$

where c is the speed of light in a vacuum. This equation is derived by considering the law of conservation of energy for the reaction in part (a). By analogy with Equation 28,

$$\begin{array}{l}\text{energy} \\ \text{equivalent to} \\ \text{rest mass of} \\ ^{212}_{84}\text{Po}\end{array} = \begin{array}{l}\text{energy} \\ \text{equivalent to} \\ \text{rest mass of} \\ ^{208}_{82}\text{Pb}\end{array}$$

$$+ \begin{array}{l}\text{energy} \\ \text{equivalent to} \\ \text{rest mass of} \\ ^{4}_{2}\text{He}\end{array} + \begin{array}{l}\text{kinetic} \\ \text{energy of} \\ ^{208}_{82}\text{Pb and} \\ ^{4}_{2}\text{He}\end{array}$$

SAQ 10 β^+-decay; $^{37}_{20}\text{Ca} \longrightarrow {}^{37}_{19}\text{K} + {}^{0}_{1}\text{e}^+ + \nu_e$

The potassium nucleus that is formed contains 19 protons and $37 - 19 = 18$ neutrons. The original isotope contained only 17 neutrons so, in this decay, a neutron must somehow have been created. This happens in β^+-decay when a proton in the original nucleus transforms into a neutron, with the emission of a positron and an electron neutrino. The mass number of the calcium isotope will be the same as that of the potassium isotope because the *total* number of protons and neutrons will be the same in both nuclei. Hence, the equation that describes the β^+-decay is

$$^{37}_{20}\text{Ca} \longrightarrow {}^{37}_{19}\text{K} + {}^{0}_{1}\text{e}^+ + \nu_e$$

SAQ 11 In radioactive γ-decay, a photon (γ-ray) is emitted when a proton or neutron in a *nucleus* makes a transition from a higher energy level to a lower energy level, whereas when visible light is emitted from atoms, each photon is emitted when an electron in the *atom* makes a transition from one of its energy levels to another lower energy level. Because the energy differences of nuclear energy levels are normally much greater than those of atomic energy levels, a photon emitted in γ-decay normally has a much greater energy than a photon emitted in an electronic transition.

SAQ 12 Statement (c) is correct (see Figure 42).

Statement (a) is false: ionizing radiation is radiation that can ionize matter. The types of ionizing radiation include α-, β^--, and β^+-particles, none of which is a type of electromagnetic radiation. Statement (b) is false: the damaged DNA molecule *may* rejoin. Statement (d) is false: for example, if the cell is a gamete, a change in the cell's structure may lead to inherited disorders in descendants.

SAQ 13 (a) The difference between spontaneous fission and induced fission is that the former occurs spontaneously, as the name suggests, whereas the latter

can occur only when energy is transferred to the nucleus concerned.

(b) $^{236}_{92}\text{U} \longrightarrow {}^{56}_{26}\text{Fe} + {}^{180}_{66}\text{Dy}$

In order to answer this question, it is a good idea to begin by representing the reaction as

$$^{236}_{92}\text{U} \longrightarrow {}^{A}_{26}\text{Fe} + {}^{180}_{Z}\text{Dy}$$

where the mass number of the formed nucleus of iron is denoted by A and the atomic number of the formed nucleus of dysprosium is denoted by Z. Because the total number of protons and neutrons and the total number of protons are the same before the reaction as they are afterwards, it is possible to calculate A and Z.

To find A: $236 = A + 180$, therefore $A = 56$

To find Z: $92 = 26 + Z$, therefore $Z = 66$

Hence, the equation of this reaction is:

$$^{236}_{92}\text{U} \longrightarrow {}^{56}_{26}\text{Fe} + {}^{180}_{66}\text{Dy}$$

SAQ 14 (a) The equation that describes this fusion is

$$^{3}_{2}\text{He} + {}^{3}_{2}\text{He} \longrightarrow 2{}^{1}_{1}\text{H} + {}^{4}_{2}\text{He}$$

(b) No, the total rest mass of the nuclei is not conserved. It is easy to see this by writing down the energy conservation equation for the reaction:

$$\begin{array}{l}\text{energy equivalent} \\ \text{to the total} \\ \text{rest mass of the} \\ \text{two } {}^{3}_{2}\text{H nuclei}\end{array} = \begin{array}{l}\text{energy equivalent} \\ \text{to the sum of the} \\ \text{rest masses of the} \\ \text{two } {}^{1}_{1}\text{H nuclei and} \\ \text{the } {}^{4}_{2}\text{He nucleus}\end{array} + \begin{array}{l}\text{energy} \\ \text{released} \\ \text{in the} \\ \text{reaction}\end{array}$$

Because energy is released in the reaction, the energy equivalent to the total rest mass before the reaction must be greater than the energy equivalent to the total rest mass after the reaction. Because Einstein's equation says that the energy equivalent to mass is directly proportional to mass ($E = mc^2$), it follows that the total rest mass before the reaction must itself be greater than the total rest mass after the reaction. (This result is generally true for any reaction in which energy is released.)

ACKNOWLEDGEMENTS

The Course Team would like to thank Andrew Mill for his considerable contribution to the preparation of the material on the hazards of radioactivity. The Team is also grateful to Peter Harbour for his comments on Section 6.

Grateful acknowledgement is made to the following sources for permission to use material in this Unit:

Figure 39 Associated Press; *Figure 41(a)* Berkeley Nuclear Laboratories; *Figures 41(b)* and *42* National Radiological Protection Board; *Figure 46* Argonne National Laboratory; *Figure 47* United Kingdom Atomic Energy Authority.

INDEX FOR UNIT 31

THE OPEN UNIVERSITY
A SCIENCE FOUNDATION COURSE

UNIT 32 THE SEARCH FOR FUNDAMENTAL PARTICLES

STUDY GUIDE

This Unit, which concerns particle physics, has two components: the text and a TV programme 'The search for the W and Z'.

The first point to make about the subject matter of this Unit is that it is in no sense 'wrapped up'—when you are studying the Unit, you will come across a number of questions that have yet to be answered. We shall draw attention to some of these questions and you may well pose some additional ones for yourself. Our account of the search for fundamental particles may not be sufficiently detailed for your taste, so to help to assuage any appetite you may develop for more material on this subject, we have provided suggestions for further reading near the end of the text.

The TV programme mainly concerns material in Section 7 of the text. You can, however, watch the programme with profit at any stage in your studies of the Unit.

Finally, a few words about the unfamiliar particles that you will be meeting in this Unit. You do not need to remember the names of all these particles—you are only required to commit to memory the names of the three *types* of particle that are currently believed to be fundamental, that is, leptons, quarks and gauge bosons.

FUNDAMENTAL PARTICLE

I INTRODUCTION

fundamental Of the groundwork, going to the root of the matter, serving as a base or foundation, essential, primary, original, from which others are derived ...

The Concise Oxford Dictionary, Oxford University Press (1982)

In the world around us, there is a wide variety of inanimate and living matter—plants, animals, rocks, water and so on. But what do these different types of matter ultimately consist of? That question, as you have already seen in this Course, can be answered at several different levels (Figure 1).

All rocks and living organisms are made of chemical compounds, which are really just combinations of atoms, which are in turn simply combinations of electrons, protons and neutrons. Hence, beneath the diversity of the matter around us is an apparent simplicity. But is this the most fundamental possible picture of matter, or do electrons, protons and neutrons themselves have constituents? This is one of the questions that will be addressed in this Unit in our discussion of the search for **fundamental particles**—particles that have *no* constituents (as far as can be told). Such particles are often said to be point-like because they are envisaged to exist only at 'points' in space and to have no shape or size.

The word particle has a special meaning in this Unit—it means 'an entity that is smaller than or has approximately the same size as a proton'. It has been found that there are hundreds of such particles, but that *only very few of them appear to be fundamental*. For example, you will see in this Unit that the electron is currently believed to be fundamental, but the proton and neutron are not, because they have been shown to have constituents.

FIGURE 1 Matter consists of atoms which in turn have constituents. Atoms that are heavier than the hydrogen atom consist of electrons and a nucleus containing protons and neutrons. Do electrons, protons and neutrons have constituents?

PARTICLE (HIGH-ENERGY)
PHYSICS

FUNDAMENTAL
INTERACTION

COSMIC RAYS

The search for fundamental particles involves the interplay of theory and experiment. As you will see in Section 2, the experiments are normally carried out with beams of high-energy particles, which is why the subject matter of this Unit is usually called **particle physics** or **high-energy physics** (the two terms are synonymous). The beams of particles are produced with the aid of machines that accelerate particles to speeds extremely close to the speed of light in a vacuum. In most of these experiments, a beam of particles is directed towards a target, and the subsequent collisions are monitored very carefully in order to study the interactions of particles.

Experiments such as these have led to the identification of three types of fundamental particle: leptons, quarks and gauge bosons (Figure 2). There are now known to exist several varieties of each of these three types of particle. In this Unit, you will see how the existence of several of the fundamental particles was predicted, and you will even be able to predict the existence of some of them for yourself!

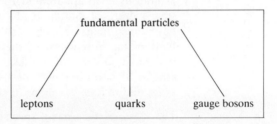

FIGURE 2 There are currently believed to be three types of fundamental particle.

How do the fundamental particles interact? It is currently believed that there are four basically different types of interaction: the gravitational, weak* and electromagnetic interactions, and the strong interaction between quarks (Figure 3). These are known as the **fundamental interactions**, because none of them can yet be understood theoretically in terms of a more basic interaction (just as a fundamental *particle* does not consist of more basic particles).

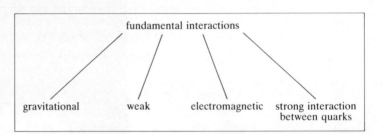

FIGURE 3 There are currently believed to be four types of fundamental interaction.

You have met two of these types of interaction before in this Course. The gravitational interaction (Unit 3), which is experienced by all particles, is responsible for 'holding' you to the ground; the electromagnetic interaction (Units 5–6) is a type of interaction in which any fundamental particle with electrical charge can participate, and is responsible for the structures of atoms and molecules. As you will see later, the strong interaction between quarks is related to the strong interaction that binds together protons and neutrons in nuclei (Unit 31), and the weak interaction is responsible for radioactive β-decay.

The basic structure of this text is very simple. We begin by introducing leptons and identifying the four leptons that were known to exist in 1974. Then we consider in detail particles called hadrons and this leads us to introduce quarks and to identify the first three types of quark that were postulated. Next, the story of leptons and quarks is brought up to date by showing how the existence of more of them has been correctly predicted.

---

* The weak interaction has nothing to do with the so-called weak bonds which you met in some of the biology and chemistry Units. These bonds are, in fundamental terms, electromagnetic in nature.

We then go on to discuss the interactions of fundamental particles and, in doing so, introduce the gauge bosons. Finally, we attempt to put the subject of particle physics into perspective relative to the other branches of science that you have met in the Course.

This material may appear to you to be somewhat abstruse and remote from everyday experience. Why have we chosen to end the Course in this way? Well, there are several reasons. First, we want you to see the most fundamental possible picture of matter that can be given according to the present state of scientific knowledge. Second, particle physics is an excellent example of a modern branch of science in which great progress has been made as a result of close cooperation between theorists and experimenters. In a single Unit at Foundation level, we cannot hope to do justice to the mathematical beauty of the theories of high-energy physics, or to the ingenious design of the apparatus used to investigate the behaviour of fundamental particles. However, we have tried to give an idea of the achievements of both theorists and experimenters, and of the extent to which these achievements have been made possible by these two groups of scientists working together.

Finally, we feel that your study of the physical sciences in this Course will be truthful to the continuing scientific quest only if it ends on a note of uncertainty. It should already be clear to you how much more remains to be understood and explained in the *Earth* and *life* sciences. We hope that by the end of this Unit you will appreciate that there are also many important and unanswered questions in the *physical* sciences. These questions are being tackled today in the same spirit of enquiry that informed the study of the planets in the 17th century and the study of atoms in the first half of this century.

Of all the Units of S102, this one contains the most science that could *not* have been taught to a student of S101, because it was not known in 1979, when S101 was first presented. By the same token, a student of S103 will be better placed than you are now to discuss fundamental particles, by virtue of the scientific work going on at this very minute in universities and other institutions throughout the world.

SAQ I   Which, if any, of the following entities is an example of a fundamental particle? (a) A chlorine molecule; (b) a helium atom; (c) a uranium nucleus.

2 OBSERVING PARTICLES

From the 1930s to the 1950s, most information concerning new particles came from studies of **cosmic rays**, the high-energy particles (mostly protons) that originated in distant parts of the Universe, probably in explosions of stars. A single cosmic ray particle can have a kinetic energy as high as 10^{21} eV, or 160 J, approximately the kinetic energy of a cricket ball delivered by a fast bowler. However, the problem with studying such particles is that it cannot be determined in advance where, when, or with what energy they will arrive.

In order to investigate systematically the behaviour of particles, reliable and intense sources of high-energy particles are required. It has been found that one of the best ways of studying these particles is to make them collide with other matter and then to examine the outcome of such close encounters. In order to study the collisions, scientists and technologists have collaborated to produce high-energy particle accelerators and detectors, and it is with these devices that most investigations of particles are currently carried out.

In this Section, we shall begin by outlining what can happen when two particles collide at high energy, in order to show why studies of collisions are such a fruitful source of information about new particles. Then we shall describe briefly how collisions are produced and studied using accelerators and detectors.

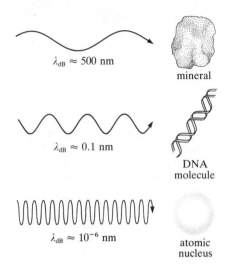

FIGURE 4   The shorter the de Broglie wavelength of a probe, the finer the detail that it can resolve. (Note that this diagram is not drawn to scale.)

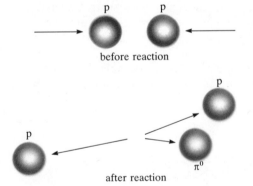

FIGURE 5   If two protons collide at sufficiently high energy, it is possible that a π^0 particle can be created. The energy of the π^0 is derived from some of the energy of the incident protons.

2.1 PARTICLE COLLISIONS AT HIGH ENERGIES

To investigate the structure of matter at the deepest possible level, matter is bombarded with particles of the highest possible energy. To understand why this is necessary remember how scientists have learnt about the structures of minerals, of the DNA molecule and of atomic nuclei (Figure 4). As you saw in the Earth sciences experiment at Summer School, the mineral composition of rocks can be investigated using visible light, whose de Broglie wavelength of approximately 500 nm is small enough to reveal the structures of rocks. In Unit 24, you saw that the molecular structure of DNA was discovered by using X-rays of much shorter de Broglie wavelength, approximately 0.1 nm. The existence and approximate size of atomic nuclei were determined by bombarding matter with α-particles of even shorter de Broglie wavelength, approximately 10^{-6} nm. These examples illustrate the important idea that the shorter the de Broglie wavelength of a probe, the finer is the detail that it can resolve.

It should now be clear that to learn about the structure of matter at the deepest possible level, *it is necessary to use particles that have the shortest possible de Broglie wavelength*. The formula for de Broglie wavelength:

$$\lambda_{dB} = \frac{h}{p}. \tag{1}$$

shows that the *shortest* possible de Broglie wavelength corresponds to the *highest* possible magnitude p of momentum. And because momentum increases with kinetic energy, it follows that the shortest possible de Broglie wavelength corresponds to the highest possible energy. Hence, in order to investigate the structure of matter with the highest possible resolution using a beam of particles, it is necessary to use particles that have the highest possible energy.

For example, the structure of protons can be investigated by bombarding them with other particles (for example other protons) that have very high energy. In such high-energy collisions between protons, something quite remarkable can happen: *during the collision, new particles* (different from the original protons) *can be formed*. For example, in one commonly observed reaction, a high-energy proton collides with a stationary proton and, during the collision, another particle called a π^0 (pronounced pi zero) is formed, seemingly out of thin air. (You will learn more about the π^0 in Section 4.) This reaction, illustrated in Figure 5, can be written conveniently as an equation:

$$p + p \rightarrow p + p + \pi^0 \tag{2}$$

The π^0 has a rest mass of approximately one-seventh of that of the proton, so the total rest mass of the particles after the collision is actually *greater* than the total rest mass of particles before the collision! This is, in terms of everyday experience, an amazing phenomenon. Think how surprised you would be if you saw, as a result of a collision between two cricket balls, a golf ball emerge out of thin air!

How can a particle be produced in a collision between two other particles? The answer is provided by Einstein's special theory of relativity, according to which an amount of energy has an equivalent mass (Unit 31). More specifically, the theory says that the mass m that is equivalent to energy E is E/c^2, so

$$E = mc^2 \tag{3}$$

where c is the speed of light in a vacuum. It is therefore easy to understand how the π^0 particle is produced in a high-energy collision (Equation 2): the energy equivalent to the rest mass of the particle is derived from some of the kinetic energy of the high-energy proton that collided with the stationary proton. As always, energy is conserved:

energy equivalent to total rest mass of original protons	kinetic + energy of the original protons	energy equivalent to total rest = mass of the two protons and the π^0	kinetic energy + of the two protons and π^0 formed

Note that the π^0 particle can be formed only if the total kinetic energy of the original protons is sufficiently high. Indeed, the greater the total kinetic energy of the original protons, the more energy is 'available' for the production of new particles.

These arguments apply equally well to all high-energy collisions between particles: *in a sufficiently high-energy collision between two particles, other particles can be created, the energy of the rest mass of each of these newly created particles being derived from some of the kinetic energy of the original particles.*

Just as energy is conserved in every collision, so momentum is always conserved (provided that no unbalanced force acts on the particles). Energy and momentum are examples of conserved *dynamical* quantities; that is, conserved quantities that are associated with the motion of the particles concerned. You will see shortly that there are other types of conserved quantity that *have nothing to do with motion*.

We shall describe shortly how high-energy collisions are studied—how the particle beams are produced, and how the collisions are observed. But now we must pause for a moment to introduce the units of energy and mass that are commonly used in particle physics.

2.2 CONVENIENT UNITS OF ENERGY AND MASS

In Unit 31, you saw that the energies associated with atomic electrons are typically of the order of between 1 and 1 000 eV, whereas the energies associated with atomic nuclei are typically of the order of *millions* of electronvolts, MeV (Figure 6). If we want to investigate the structure of matter at the deepest possible level, we must use even higher energies, typically greater than or of the order of a thousand million electronvolts, 10^9 eV. This multiple of the electronvolt is called the gigaelectronvolt (GeV) and it is a standard unit of energy in particle physics:

$$1\,\text{GeV} = 10^9\,\text{eV} \tag{4}$$

What about units of mass? It is usual in high-energy physics to measure mass not in units of kilograms but in units of GeV/c^2. In order to see why, consider the rest mass m_p of the proton, $m_p \approx 1.67 \times 10^{-27}$ kg. Let us find the energy $m_p c^2$ that, according to Einstein's equation (Equation 3), is equivalent to the rest mass of the proton:

$$m_p c^2 \approx (1.67 \times 10^{-27}\,\text{kg}) \times (3.00 \times 10^8\,\text{m s}^{-1})^2$$
$$\approx 1.50 \times 10^{-10}\,\text{J}$$

Because $1\,\text{eV} \approx 1.60 \times 10^{-19}$ J,

$$m_p c^2 \approx \frac{1.50 \times 10^{-10}\,\text{J}}{1.60 \times 10^{-19}\,\text{J eV}^{-1}}$$

i.e. $m_p c^2 \approx 9.4 \times 10^8$ eV

and, because $1\,\text{GeV} = 10^9$ eV (Equation 4),

$$m_p c^2 \approx 0.94\,\text{GeV}$$

so $m_p \approx 0.94\,\text{GeV}/c^2$

This calculation shows that the rest mass of the proton is, roughly speaking, $1\,\text{GeV}/c^2$. Hence, the GeV/c^2 is a very convenient unit in which to measure the rest mass of the proton—it is much easier to remember that the rest mass of the proton is roughly $1\,\text{GeV}/c^2$, than it is to remember that its value is 1.67×10^{-27} kg!

You will see later that there exist many particles with rest masses that are, within an order of magnitude, the same as the rest mass of the proton. That is why particle physicists find the GeV/c^2 such a convenient unit of mass, and why we shall always use this unit in this text. In summary, energy will be measured in units of GeV, mass will be measured in units of GeV/c^2.

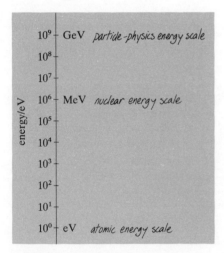

FIGURE 6 The energy scales of atomic, nuclear and particle physics.

FIGURE 7   Part of the linear accelerator at SLAC in Stanford, California.

FIGURE 8   There are several synchrotrons at the European Organization for Nuclear Research (CERN) at Geneva, Switzerland. The Large Electron-Positron storage ring (LEP) is indicated by the largest circle. The Super Proton Synchrotron (SPS) is in an underground tunnel, indicated by the second largest circle.

2.3 ACCELERATORS

In particle-physics laboratories, beams of electrically-charged particles are produced using accelerators, which can be classified into two basic types: linear and circular. There is an example of a **linear accelerator** in California at the Stanford Linear Accelerator Centre, SLAC. In this machine, electrons are accelerated by electrical forces down a long tube (Figure 7) in which there is, to most intents and purposes, a vacuum, i.e. almost nothing with which the particles can collide. At the end of their 3 km journey, the electrons have a kinetic energy of approximately 50 GeV, and they are travelling at very nearly the speed of light in a vacuum. It is worth noting that no matter how much electrons (or any other particles with non-zero rest mass) are accelerated, they never reach the speed of light in a vacuum. This is one of the predictions of the special theory of relativity.

Linear accelerators have important limitations. For example, it is unlikely that the maximum kinetic energy to which particles can be accelerated will (in the near future) be much greater than the 50 GeV achieved at Stanford, unless there is an unforeseen technological breakthrough. Much higher energies can be achieved relatively easily using circular (or nearly circular) accelerators called **synchrotrons**. Figure 8 shows the two synchrotrons at the European Organization for Nuclear Research (CERN) in Geneva, Switzerland.

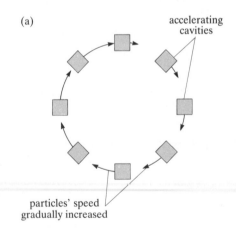

(a)

accelerating cavities

particles' speed gradually increased

(b)

FIGURE 9   (a) In a synchrotron, particles are repeatedly accelerated by the same cavities. (b) An analogy for the basic operation of a synchrotron.

The basic idea behind the design of synchrotrons is quite simple. A batch of particles is made to travel many times in a circular (or nearly circular) path, in a tube in which there is (very nearly) a vacuum. At various points on the path are special devices, called 'cavities', which provide alternating electrical forces to accelerate the protons. Because the particles travel round the path many times, a given cavity can be used to accelerate them many times in succession (Figure 9a). The oscillations of the electrical forces in each cavity have to be *synchronized* with the arrival of the batch of particles so that each time they pass through, they gain energy—hence the name of the machine. This process of synchronized particle acceleration is somewhat analogous to the procedure shown in Figure 9b.

What makes the particles travel in a circular (or nearly circular) orbit? You know from Unit 3 that the force on a particle moving in a circular orbit is always directed towards the centre of the circle. In a synchrotron, the force

LINEAR ACCELERATOR

SYNCHROTRON

FIXED-TARGET EXPERIMENTS

COLLIDING-BEAM EXPERIMENTS

(a)

fixed-target

(b)

colliding-beam

FIGURE 10   Two basic types of collisions studied in particle-physics experiments: (a) fixed-target, (b) colliding-beam.

that keeps the particles travelling in a circular (or nearly circular) path is provided by powerful magnets placed round the path. (You first met the force on charged particles due to a magnetic field in Units 5–6.)

As the kinetic energy of the particles gradually increases, an increasing force is required to keep them moving in the same path, so the strength of the magnetic field must constantly be increased during the process of acceleration. This is achieved by increasing the electric currents flowing in coils that are wound round the iron from which the magnets are made. So you can see that it takes a great deal of technological ingenuity to realize the simple idea expressed in Figure 9.

Remember that the beam of particles is produced so that its collision with a target can be observed. In modern experiments, both fixed and moving targets are used. **Fixed-target experiments** involve, as the name suggests, the directing of a high-energy beam of particles from an accelerator (linear or circular) towards a stationary target (Figure 10a). In contrast, moving-target experiments involve the collision of a beam of particles with another beam that is moving in the opposite (or nearly opposite) direction (Figure 10b). These **colliding-beam experiments** are usually carried out with particles that have been accelerated in synchrotrons.

Colliding-beam experiments have an important advantage over fixed-target experiments: in the former, a higher proportion of the particles' total kinetic energy is available for the production of particles than is the case in the latter type of experiment (assuming that the comparison is made for collisions that involve the same total kinetic energy). In order to understand this, think about the momenta and energies involved in the two types of experiment, before and after the beam and target particles collide.

Consider first a fixed-target experiment (Figure 11a) between a beam particle, with kinetic energy E_k and momentum of magnitude p, and a target (which of course has zero kinetic energy and momentum because it is stationary). Momentum is conserved in the collision: the total momentum of the particles produced in the collision must be the same as the total momentum of the particles before the collision. This implies that the particles (or particle) produced in the collision must *also* have kinetic energy (Figure 11a). Hence, *in a fixed-target experiment, some of the kinetic energy of the beam must always be used in 'giving' kinetic energy to the produced particles (or particle).*

Now consider an analogous colliding-beam experiment that involves the same initial kinetic energy, shared equally between the beam and target particles which have momenta that are of the *same magnitude* but are in *opposite directions*, so that the *total* momentum is zero. The law of conservation of momentum says that the total momentum of the particle (or particles) produced in the collision must also be zero. If a single particle were produced, it would be stationary (Figure 11b)—*all* of the kinetic energy of the original beam and target would have been converted into the energy of the rest mass of the produced particle!

It is actually extremely rare for a *single* particle to be produced in this way. Normally several particles are produced and some of the original particles' kinetic energy is used to give kinetic energy to the produced particles.

FIGURE 11   In a colliding-beam experiment that involves particles that have total kinetic energy E_k, a higher proportion of this energy is available for the production of particles during the collision than is the case in an analogous fixed-target experiment that involves the same particles with the same total kinetic energy E_k.

(a)

(b)

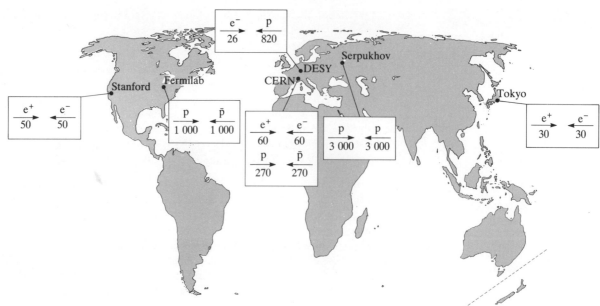

FIGURE 12   The locations of the highest-energy particle accelerators that will used in the 1980s and 90s. For each laboratory, we have shown the highest-energy collisions that it can study. (The numbers below the horizontal arrows refer to the maximum energy, in units of GeV, to which the particle identified above the arrow can be accelerated.) The symbol $\bar{p}$ denotes an antiproton, which you will meet later, and e^+ denotes a positron (see Unit 31).

However, it is true in general that in a colliding-beam experiment that involves particles with total kinetic energy E_k, a higher proportion of this energy is available for the production of particles during the collision than is the case in an analogous fixed-target experiment involving the same particles with the same total kinetic energy E_k.

This important advantage of colliding-beam experiments has been used to good effect in recent years—as you will see later, no fewer than four fundamental particles have been discovered recently in this type of experiment! However, it would be wrong to give the impression that colliding-beam experiments are invariably superior to experiments involving fixed targets. Indeed, for many purposes, fixed-target experiments are preferable. For example, it turns out that they normally enable many more collisions to be achieved (in a given time) between the beam and the target. Also, the high-energy particles produced in fixed-target experiments are often used to provide the *beams* for other experiments.

Such is the enormous expense of building and operating high-energy particle accelerators that the world has only relatively few particle-physics laboratories. In Figure 12, you can see the locations of the laboratories used in the 1980s and 90s to study collisions at the highest possible energies. The Figure also shows the type of collisions that each laboratory is equipped to study.

2.4 DETECTORS

DRIFT CHAMBER

The interaction between a beam and a target particle normally takes place in approximately 10^{-23} s (ten millionths of a millionth of a millionth of a millionth of a second) and the particles produced travel at speeds close to the speed of light in a vacuum, approximately $3 \times 10^8 \, \mathrm{m \, s^{-1}}$! It is the function of particle detectors to provide a record of the outcome of such collisions.

Most detectors are able to record the tracks only of electrically charged particles. An example of such a record is given in Figure 13, in which you can see the tracks of the charged particles produced in a colliding beam experiment involving two particles that each had an energy of 270 GeV. The record in Figure 13 was produced by a type of detector known as a **drift chamber** (Figure 14).

Each cylindrical drift chamber is subject to a constant horizontal magnetic field, and each one contains an array of closely spaced horizontal wires and a gaseous mixture of argon and ethane at low pressure. A high-energy elec-

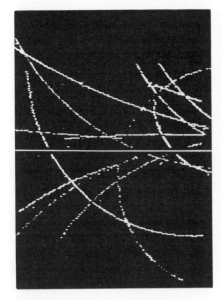
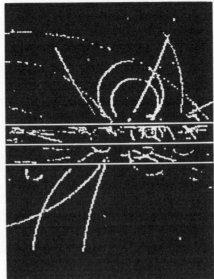
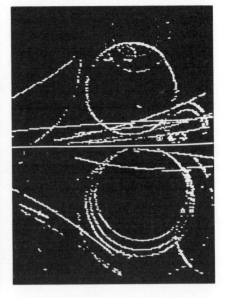

FIGURE 13 Tracks of charged particles that were produced in a head-on collision between two particles that each had an energy of 270 GeV.

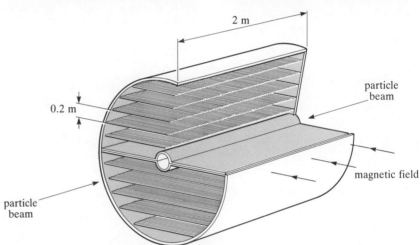

FIGURE 14 A drift chamber. Three of these chambers were used to produce the record shown in Figure 13.

FIGURE 15 This huge bubble chamber (known as BEBC, the Big European Bubble Chamber) was used at CERN between 1973 and 1984. It is now no longer in operation. The chamber was used to take more than six million photographs of particle interactions. (For scale, note the technician at the bottom right of the photograph.)

trically charged particle that passes through the chamber ionizes the gas molecules in its path, which then drift to the wires, depositing their charge. The pattern of charges appearing on many wires is recorded electronically and this is later analysed by computer to reconstruct the path of the particle. This apparatus actually enables the determination of the paths of *all* of the charged particles produced in a collision, during the first two millionths of a second after the collision takes place.

After the tracks have been determined, it is necessary to identify the particles that are produced. Also, the energies of the particles are determined, and one way in which this can be done is by measuring the curvatures of their tracks in the magnetic field. The process of data-collecting and analysis is extremely subtle and complicated, and we cannot possibly do justice here to the experimental skills involved. Suffice it to say that, given a visual record such as the one in Figure 13, experimenters can deduce many details about the outcome of the collision. You will see in Section 7 (and in the TV programme) that experimenters at the CERN laboratory in Geneva were able in 1983 to use records similar to the one in Figure 13 to discover two new fundamental particles.

We have discussed only the drift chamber detector, but you should remember that this is not by any means the only type of detector used in particle-physics laboratories. There are several other types of charged-particle detector, and you have already met one in Unit 30—the bubble chamber (Figure 15). Remember, in this device, the tracks of charged particles are observed when they interact with liquid hydrogen that is just below its boiling temperature. There is an example of a bubble chamber photograph on the front cover of these Units.

LEPTON

ELECTRON

NEUTRINO

Finally, it is worth mentioning that experimenters have also found ways of observing, albeit indirectly, the *uncharged* (i.e. electrically neutral) particles that are involved in collisions. Although the tracks of such particles cannot be recorded (because they do not cause ionizations), it is nevertheless possible to determine their energy and momentum.

SUMMARY OF SECTION 2

1   By bombarding matter with particles that have the shortest possible de Broglie wavelength, i.e. the highest possible energy, the structure of matter can be investigated at the deepest possible level.

2   When two particles collide at sufficiently high energy, other particles can be produced: some of the kinetic energy of the original particles is converted into the energy equivalent to the rest masses of the newly formed particles.

3   In particle physics, it is convenient to measure energy in units of GeV and to measure mass in units of GeV/c^2.

4   There are two basic types of particle accelerator: linear and circular. Modern accelerators produce beams of particles that have energies of several GeV or more.

5   There are two types of experiment: fixed-target and colliding beam. The latter type is better for the purpose of producing particles in the collision.

6   Most particle detectors (e.g. drift chambers and bubble chambers) are designed to record the tracks of the electrically charged particles that are produced in collisions.

SAQ 2   When two particles collide at high energy, other particles can be produced apparently 'out of thin air'. Explain, in one or two sentences, why this is possible.

SAQ 3   This question concerns the π^0 particle, which has a rest mass of approximately 2.41×10^{-28} kg.
(a) Can a π^0 leave a track in a drift chamber?
(b) Can the particle be accelerated to a speed of $4 \times 10^8 \, m \, s^{-1}$?
(c) What is the rest mass of this particle in units of GeV/c^2? (Hint: Refer to the back cover, which tells you how many kilograms are equivalent to $1 \, GeV/c^2$.)

SAQ 4   In a colliding-beam experiment at CERN, a particle with a kinetic energy of 270 GeV collides head-on with another particle that has the same kinetic energy.

(a) What is the total kinetic energy of the particles (i) in units of GeV and (ii) in units of joules?
(b) What is the total momentum of the particles?

3 LEPTONS

After we have explained how particles are named in high-energy physics, a family of four **leptons** will be introduced. (The meaning of the term 'lepton' will be made clear later.) Each of these particles is currently believed to be fundamental (i.e. to have no constituents) and each has a corresponding *anti*particle. The properties of these antiparticles will be discussed and then the interactions of the leptons (and their antiparticles) will be considered briefly.

3.1 SYMBOLIZING PARTICLES

In this Section, the simple system that is conventionally used in high-energy physics to symbolize particles will be introduced. The system, which will be used in this Unit, *applies to all types of observed particle, not only to leptons.*

The symbol that is used to denote a given particle normally consists of a letter (or letters) from the Greek or Roman alphabet with a superscript that indicates whether the particle's charge is positive, negative or zero. If there is no superscript, you can normally take it for granted that the particle is electrically neutral. (A common exception is the proton, which, as you know, is denoted simply by p.) Also, it is worthwhile to remember that the charge of every observed particle is always a positive or negative multiple of the charge of the proton, which is conventionally denoted by the italic letter e (e is approximately 1.602×10^{-19} coulombs).

When you come across the name of an unfamiliar particle, this notation is particularly useful because it enables you to deduce the particle's charge immediately. For example, consider the particles τ^-, K^+ and Z, which you will meet later in the Unit:

- The τ^- has charge $-e$ (i.e. approximately -1.602×10^{-19} C).
- The K^+ has charge $+e$ (i.e. approximately $+1.602 \times 10^{-19}$ C).
- The Z has no charge. (The absence of a superscript indicates that the particle is electrically neutral.)

3.2 FOUR LEPTONS AND THEIR ANTIPARTICLES

Perhaps the most familiar member of the lepton family is the **electron** e^-, which was discovered in 1897 by the English physicist J. J. Thomson and which is now known to be a constituent of every atom. Thomson found that the electron has a rest mass of approximately 5.11×10^{-4} GeV/c^2 and a charge of approximately -1.60×10^{-19} C*. These are the smallest non-zero values of rest mass and charge that have ever been measured, and this lends credence to the idea that the electron has no observable constituents.

In 1937, another negatively charged lepton was discovered unexpectedly in studies of the collisions between cosmic rays and nuclei in the Earth's upper atmosphere. This new lepton was later called the μ^-, pronounced mu minus. The μ^-, which is now believed to be a fundamental particle, has the same charge as the electron but its rest mass is approximately 207 times that of the electron. One of the first μ^- tracks to be observed is shown in Figure 16.

It was not long before it was found that there existed not only charged leptons but also neutral varieties. In 1931, the physicist Wolfgang Pauli predicted the existence of the **neutrino**, a particle that he suggested would be observed to have zero charge and zero rest mass. By 1956, the existence of Pauli's neutrino ν_e, associated with the electron, had been established and it had been shown that such a neutrino is emitted in each radioactive β^+-decay (Unit 31). Six years later, experimenters also demonstrated that there exists *another* neutrino ν_μ, which is associated with the μ^-.

Each type of neutrino is currently believed to be a fundamental particle, and each one has zero charge and a rest mass that is compatible with zero. However, the results of current experiments do not rule out the possibility of the neutrinos' each having a non-zero rest mass. (All that is known for

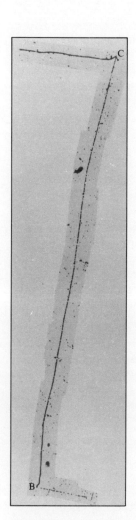

FIGURE 16 The track BC was one of the first μ^- tracks to be observed. The material in which the particle is travelling is a specially sensitized photographic emulsion.

* As you saw in Units 11–12, the electron also has spin. This property is shared by many other particles, notably by all other leptons, but we shall not consider it further in this Unit.

ANTIPARTICLE

sure is that the rest mass of the electron neutrino v_e is no greater than $4.6 \times 10^{-8}\,\text{GeV}/c^2$ and the rest mass of the muon neutrino v_μ is no greater than $2.5 \times 10^{-4}\,\text{GeV}/c^2$.)

Neutrinos can be produced artificially in particle accelerators, but they also occur naturally in abundance. For example, the Sun continuously emits neutrinos (mainly electron neutrinos) at a prodigous rate: approximately 10^{12} (a million million) pass through you every second. They come up through your bed at night, and they rain down on you during the day (Figure 17).

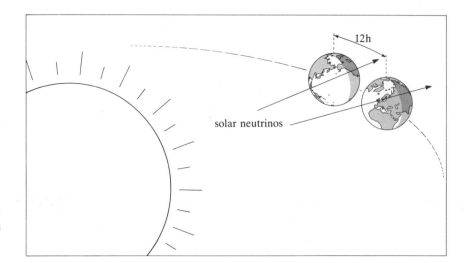

FIGURE 17 Solar neutrinos come up through your bed at night and they rain down on you during the day. (This Figure is not drawn to scale.)

You are probably surprised to learn that you are penetrated continuously in this way, and that this has been going on since you were conceived. Why have you not noticed this before? Why are neutrinos so elusive? These questions will be answered shortly, but let us now pause briefly to recap the leptons that you have met so far: the negatively charged electron e^- and mu minus μ^-, and their associated neutrinos, v_e and v_μ. These fundamental particles are normally grouped together like this:

$$\begin{pmatrix} e^- & \mu^- \\ v_e & v_\mu \end{pmatrix}$$

But that is not the end of the story: for each of these four leptons there exists a corresponding **antiparticle** (antilepton). The concept of an anti-particle (antimatter) was introduced in 1928 by the great English theoretical physicist Paul Dirac. He predicted, using quantum mechanics and the special theory of relativity, that there should exist an antiparticle of the electron, with precisely the same rest mass as the electron but with precisely the opposite charge. At the time, no one had ever observed such an anti-particle, and Dirac's prediction was viewed with considerable scepticism.

Four years later in California, Carl Anderson, a young American experi-menter working on cosmic-ray physics, observed the track AB shown in Figure 18. On studying the track, Anderson concluded that it was left by a particle that had never before been detected. He wrote that the track

> seemed to be interpretable only on the basis of the existence .... of a particle carrying a positive charge but having a mass of the same order of magnitude as that normally possessed by a free negative electron.

Anderson, unaware of Dirac's theoretical work, did not realize that he had been the first person ever to detect antimatter! The entity that he had observed, which he called the positron e^+, was actually the antiparticle of the electron. (You may remember from Unit 31 that a positron is emitted in each radioactive β^+-decay.)

It was later shown theoretically, using quantum mechanics in conjunction with the special theory of relativity, that the concept of an antiparticle applies not just to the electron, it should apply to *all* fundamental particles.

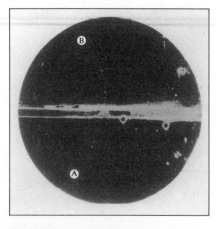

FIGURE 18 The first recorded track of a positron e^+, which in this photograph travels from A to B. The curvature of the track allowed Anderson to deduce that the entity that left the track has positive charge.

> For every fundamental particle of matter there should exist a corresponding antiparticle that is also fundamental. The particle and antiparticle have the *same* rest mass, but their other properties (e.g. charge) are *opposite*.

Using this result, it is possible to infer the existence of three more antileptons, corresponding to the μ^-, ν_e and ν_μ. The antiparticle of the μ^- is the μ^+ (the mu plus)*, and the two antineutrinos are denoted by $\bar{\nu}_e$ (the electron antineutrino) and $\bar{\nu}_\mu$ (the muon antineutrino). These antiparticles have all been observed, and they are all currently believed to be fundamental. It is conventional to group them together like this:

$$\begin{pmatrix} e^+ & \mu^+ \\ \bar{\nu}_e & \bar{\nu}_\mu \end{pmatrix}$$

You have already met electron antineutrinos in Unit 31, where you saw that one of them is emitted in each β^--decay. This type of radioactive process occurs continually within the Earth (Units 28–29), and consequently about a million of these antineutrinos emerge each second through each square centimetre of horizontal ground on the Earth's surface!

The names, rest masses and charges of the four leptons and four antileptons discussed in this Section are given in Table 1, which has, however, been left incomplete.

TABLE 1   Four leptons and four antileptons

Name	Symbol	Charge /(charge e of proton)	Rest mass /(GeV/c^2)
electron	e^-	-1	5.11×10^{-4}
electron neutrino	ν_e	0	≈ 0
mu minus	μ^-	-1	1.06×10^{-1}
muon neutrino	ν_μ	0	≈ 0
positron	e^+		
electron antineutrino	$\bar{\nu}_e$		
mu plus	μ^+		
muon antineutrino	$\bar{\nu}_\mu$		

ITQ I   Complete Table 1. (You should be able to do this without referring back to the text.)

3.3 THE INTERACTIONS OF LEPTONS AND OF ANTILEPTONS

We shall now review the ways in which leptons and antileptons can interact with each other and with other matter. Consider first the neutrinos and antineutrinos which, remember, each have zero charge and zero (or nearly zero) rest mass. In common with all other particles (and antiparticles), neutrinos and antineutrinos interact gravitationally. This is true even if (contrary to current expectations) they have precisely zero rest mass: the general theory of relativity tells us that all matter and antimatter participate in gravitational interactions, whether or not they have rest mass. You may remember from the TV programmes 'Practically speaking' and 'Voyages of Discovery' the experiment that showed that light, which consists of photons of zero rest mass, is 'bent' by the gravitational attraction of the Sun.

---

* The μ^- and μ^+ are often collectively termed muons.

WEAK INTERACTION

□ Can neutrinos and antineutrinos interact electromagnetically, i.e. do electric and magnetic forces act on them?

■ No, only electrically *charged* fundamental particles are subject to electromagnetic interactions.

It turns out that neutrinos can also interact in a way that you have not met before in this Course—via the **weak interaction**. In order to see just how feeble the weak interaction is, consider again the 10^{12} solar neutrinos that bombard you each second. These neutrinos pass through you almost as if you didn't exist; in fact, it is extremely unlikely that a single one will interact with an atom in your body. (If such an interaction did occur in your body, you certainly wouldn't come to any harm!)

Now consider the interactions of the other four leptons—the electron e^-, the mu minus particle μ^-, and their antiparticles. Because they each have electrical charge, they can interact *electromagnetically*. You may remember from Unit 9 that one of the characteristics of this type of interaction is that stationary particles with charges of the same sign repel each other, whereas stationary particles with the opposite sign attract each other.

The charged leptons (and antileptons) can interact *gravitationally* and it turns out that they can also interact *weakly* with other matter. However, the gravitational and weak interactions are considerably more feeble than the electromagnetic interaction, as you can see in Table 2, which gives the approximate relative strengths of the three basic types of interaction. The data in the Table show that the electromagnetic interaction has approximately a thousand times the strength of the weak interaction, and approximately 10^{36} times the strength of the gravitational interaction.

The feebleness of the gravitational interaction may puzzle you. If its strength is so small compared with those of the electromagnetic and weak interactions, how can it be responsible for holding you down to Earth? The answer is that you and the Earth do not usually interact electromagnetically because both are normally electrically neutral. The dominant interaction between you and the Earth is gravitational, and its magnitude is sufficient to keep you on the planet's surface only because the Earth has an enormous mass (approximately 10^{25} kg). If you were not close to an astronomical object of such a large mass, and were, say, in outer space, you would scarcely be conscious of any gravitational interaction.

If the strength of the weak interaction is 10^{33} times that of the gravitational interaction (Table 2), why aren't the effects of the weak interaction even more obvious than those of the gravitational interaction in everyday life? The answer is that the weak interaction has a *much shorter range* than the gravitational interaction—whereas the range of the weak interaction is only about 10^{-18} m (a tenth of a thousandth of the diameter of a typical nucleus), the range of the gravitational interaction is, like that of the electromagnetic interaction, infinite*.

ITQ 2   Table 3 shows the interactions of the four leptons and four antileptons introduced in this Section. Complete the Table.

The term lepton (which is taken from the Greek word for a small coin) has been used frequently in this Section, but we have not yet specified its meaning. We shall, in fact, postpone doing so until the next Section, where you will encounter particles that are *not* leptons.

TABLE 2   Relative strengths* of three fundamental interactions

Fundamental interaction	Relative strength (order of magnitude estimate)
electromagnetic	1
weak	10^{-3}
gravitational	10^{-36}

* Strictly speaking, these strengths depend on the energies with which the interactions are probed. (The strengths quoted here refer to interactions probed using an energy of 1 GeV.)

TABLE 3   Interactions of leptons and antileptons (For ITQ 2)

	Electro-magnetic	Weak	Gravit-ational
e^- e^{+} μ^- μ^+			yes
ν_e $\bar{\nu}_e$ ν_μ $\bar{\nu}_\mu$	no	yes	

* In order to see that the electromagnetic and gravitational interactions have infinite range, remember that the magnitudes of the gravitational and electrostatic forces between two particles are both inversely proportional to the square of the separation r of the particles concerned: $F \propto 1/r^2$ (Units 3 and 9 respectively), Hence F is non-zero even when r is extremely large.

SUMMARY OF SECTION 3

1   Each fundamental particle has an associated fundamental antiparticle. The particle and antiparticle have the same rest mass, but their other properties (e.g. charge) are opposite.

2   Leptons and their antiparticles, antileptons, are currently believed to be fundamental.

3   Leptons and antileptons interact gravitationally and they each also participate in electromagnetic or weak interactions (or in both).

4   The electromagnetic interaction is stronger than the weak interaction, which is in turn very much stronger than the gravitational interaction (but see the footnote to Table 2).

5   The four leptons and four antileptons discussed in this Section are

$$\begin{pmatrix} e^- & \mu^- \\ \nu_e & \nu_\mu \end{pmatrix} \qquad \begin{pmatrix} e^+ & \mu^+ \\ \bar{\nu}_e & \bar{\nu}_\mu \end{pmatrix}$$

$$\qquad\text{leptons} \qquad\qquad \text{antileptons}$$

6   Neutrinos and antineutrinos do not participate in electromagnetic interactions.

SAQ 5   Which one of the following statements about the μ^- and μ^+ is false?

(a) The μ^- and μ^+ have the same rest mass.

(b) The charge of the μ^+ is the same as that of the proton.

(c) The μ^- and μ^+ are each believed to have constituents.

(d) If a μ^- and a μ^+ were to collide, they would interact electromagnetically.

SAQ 6   This question concerns the poem *Cosmic Gall* by the American writer John Updike. First, read the poem carefully.

> Neutrinos, they are very small.
>   They have no charge and have no mass
> And do not interact at all,
> The Earth is just a silly ball
>   To them, through which they simply pass,
> Like dustmaids down a drafty hall
>   Or photons through a sheet of glass.
>   They snub the most exquisite gas,
> Ignore the most substantial wall,
>   Cold-shoulder steel and sounding brass,
> Insult the stallion in his stall,
>   And, scorning barriers of class,
> Infiltrate you and me! Like tall
> and painless guillotines, they fall
>   Down through our heads into the grass,
> At night, they enter at Nepal
>   And pierce the lover and his lass
> From underneath the bed—you call
>   It wonderful; I call it crass.

(a) Updike refers in the first three lines to the behaviour of 'neutrinos'. Are the properties mentioned in these lines shared by antineutrinos?

(b) In the third line of the poem, Updike says that neutrinos 'do not interact at all'. Why is this not scientifically correct?

(c) Why does Updike liken the passing of neutrinos through the Earth to the passing of 'photons through a sheet of glass'?

STRONG INTERACTION

HADRON

4 HADRONS

We shall now introduce another class of particles called hadrons. You will see that these particles are each characterized by several properties including 'strangeness', a word that will almost certainly have a new meaning for you when you have finished this Section! After the properties of hadrons have been discussed, we shall ask whether they are fundamental particles.

4.1 HUNDREDS OF HADRONS

You saw in Unit 31 that protons and neutrons are bound together in nuclei by the strong interaction, an interaction whose strength is much greater than that of its electromagnetic and gravitational counterparts. Now, experiments (mostly carried out using particle accelerators) have shown that the proton and neutron are only two of hundreds of particles that are subject to the **strong interaction**. These particles are collectively called **hadrons**.

> Hadrons are particles that feel the strong interaction.

Leptons are not subject to the strong interaction, and this property enables a distinction to made between hadrons and leptons.

> Leptons do *not* feel the strong interaction.

π^-	π^0	π^+
0.1396	0.1350	0.1396

n	p
0.9396	0.9383

Λ
1.116

Δ^-	Δ^0	Δ^+	Δ^{++}
1.232	1.232	1.232	1.232

K^0	K^+
0.4977	0.4937

Σ^-	Σ^0	Σ^+
1.197	1.192	1.189

ϕ
1.020

Ξ^-	Ξ^0	$\overline{K}^0$	K^-
1.315	1.321	0.4977	0.4937

FIGURE 19 Some families of hadrons. (There is no significance to the positions of the families in this Figure.) Notice that the K hadrons are actually grouped into *two* families—they differ in a fundamental property other than charge (as you will see later). The number beneath each hadron is its rest mass in units of GeV/c^2.

The symbols that represent 20 hadrons are given in Figure 19, with their respective rest masses (in units of GeV/c^2). In this Figure, all the hadrons are grouped together in families (each with at least one member) whose members have approximately (or exactly) the same rest mass. Each member is designated by the same Greek or Roman letter, and the superscript as usual denotes its charge, which of course is given in units of the charge e of the proton. (The arrangement of the families of hadrons in Figure 19 is arbitrary.)

The rest mass of each hadron in Figure 19 (and of every hadron observed to date) is non-zero and is within approximately an order of magnitude of $1\,GeV/c^2$. Hence, hadrons are generally much heavier than the leptons that you met in the previous Section. This explains why the word hadron was chosen to name this class of particles, for the word is derived from the Greek word *hadros*, which means bulky.

It turns out that all hadrons except the proton* are unstable—they sooner or later decay into other particles. The decays of hadrons are classified as strong, electromagnetic and weak. (The gravitational interactions between hadrons, and between individual particles, can be ignored as they are negligible.) These terms refer to the principal interaction involved in a particular decay. The greater the strength of the interaction, the more quickly the

* Modern theories predict that the proton is unstable, and the predictions of the theories are consistent with the experimentally determined lower limit of the proton's half-life, which is about 10^{32} years! Neutrons can be stable when they are in nuclei, but when free they decay within about 15 minutes ($n \rightarrow p + e^- + \bar{\nu}_e$).

decay normally takes place: strong decays normally take place within only 10^{-23} s of the creation of the original hadron, whereas electromagnetic and weak decays take much longer to occur (typically, 10^{-18} s and 10^{-10} s respectively). Later (Section 5) we consider β^--decay, a particularly important example of a weak decay, which you have met several times in the Course.

We shall not be much concerned in this Unit with the differences between the three types of decay, and you will not be asked to differentiate between them.

Before we go on to consider further the properties of hadrons, it is worthwhile to pause for a moment to consider the meaning of *charge*, an electrical property with which you are already familiar. When it is said that a hadron (or any other particle) has charge, a statement is implicitly being made about the effect the particle can have on other particles. For example, a π^- particle will be attracted to any positively charged particle, and it will be repelled by any negatively charged particle. On the other hand, a π^+ particle (which has the same mass as that of the π^-, but opposite charge) has a different effect on other charged particles—it is *repelled* by positively charged particles and *attracted* to negatively charged particles. The charge of a particle is simply a property (a label, if you like) that gives information about the electromagnetic effects that the particle can have on other particles, just as the mass of a particle tells us about the gravitational effects that the particle can have on other particles.

The unit used to express the numerical values of the charges of particles is not important. We are free to *choose* the charge of any charged particle as our unit of charge, then we can measure the charges of all other particles in terms of the chosen unit. As you have already seen, it is conventional to choose the charge of the proton to be $+1$.

You will see next that studies of the behaviour of hadrons have shown that each hadron is characterized not only by its charge, but also by other analogous properties.

4.2 PROPERTIES OF HADRONS

You saw in Section 2 that energy and momentum are conserved dynamical quantities: for each one, its total value before an interaction is equal to its total value afterwards. Now it is found experimentally that some collision and decay processes that *in principle* are allowed according to energy and momentum conservation, have *in practice* never been observed to occur—they appear to be 'forbidden'. In order to explain this phenomenon, it is essential to ascribe a small number of *intrinsic* properties to each hadron and to assume that each of these properties is conserved in each interaction. It is important to note that a conserved intrinsic property does not depend in any way on the motion of the hadrons.

Three intrinsic properties will now be discussed, beginning with a property that is already very familiar to you, that is, charge.

4.2.1 CHARGE AND ITS CONSERVATION

You have already seen that the electrical charge Q of each hadron is conventionally measured in units of the charge e of the proton. It has been found experimentally that, in *every* interaction that has ever been observed (between hadrons and indeed between *all* particles and antiparticles), charge is conserved—the total charge of all the particles *before* the interaction is equal to the total charge of the particles *after* the interaction. In other words, no reaction has ever been observed in which the total charge before and after the reaction are different.

BARYON NUMBER

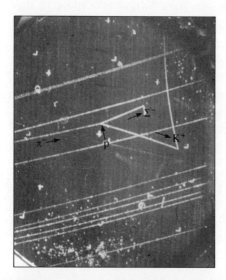

FIGURE 20   A record, obtained using a bubble chamber, of the collision between a π^- and a proton (the nucleus of a hydrogen atom in the chamber) in which a K^+ and a Σ^- are formed.

An example should make clear this idea of charge conservation. The strong interaction below, in which a π^- and a proton collide at high energy with the formation of a K^+ and a Σ^- particle, has frequently been observed (Figure 20):

$$\pi^- + p \rightarrow K^+ + \Sigma^- \qquad \text{observed}$$
$$\text{charge } Q \quad \underbrace{-1 \quad 1} \quad \underbrace{1 \quad -1}$$
$$0 \quad = \quad 0 \qquad Q \text{ conserved}$$

However, the following reaction between a π^- and a proton has *never* been observed, even when there is in principle sufficient energy available for the K^+, Σ^- and π^- to be produced:

$$\pi^- + p \nrightarrow K^+ + \Sigma^- + \pi^- \qquad \text{not observed}$$
$$\text{charge } Q \quad \underbrace{-1 \quad 1} \quad \underbrace{1 \quad -1 \quad -1}$$
$$0 \quad \neq \quad -1 \qquad Q \text{ not conserved}$$

The fact that this reaction has not been observed is easy to understand in terms of charge conservation: it does not occur because charge is not conserved in the reaction.

The law of charge conservation is extremely useful because it allows us to predict reactions that will *not* occur. For example, the law predicts that these two decays will never be observed because they contradict the law:

$$\Xi^- \nrightarrow \Lambda + \pi^+ \qquad Q \text{ not conserved}$$
$$\Sigma^+ \nrightarrow \Lambda + \pi^- \qquad Q \text{ not conserved}$$

These predictions have been borne out experimentally, because these decays have never been observed.

ITQ 3   Which one of the following reactions is forbidden because it would involve the non-conservation of charge?

(a) $p + p \rightarrow p + p$

(b) $p + p \rightarrow p + p + \pi^+ + \pi^-$

(c) $p + p \rightarrow p + p + \pi^+ + \pi^- + \pi^+$

4.2.2   BARYON NUMBER AND ITS CONSERVATION

When two protons collide at high energy and interact strongly, the reactions

$$p + p \rightarrow p + p + \pi^0 \tag{2*}$$
$$p + p \rightarrow p + p + \pi^+ + \pi^-$$

have frequently been observed to occur. Not surprising, you may think—charge is conserved in both cases. However, there are many interactions that have never been observed *even though they are allowed by charge conservation*. For example:

$$p + p \nrightarrow p + p + n \tag{5a}$$
$$p + p \nrightarrow p + p + n + n \tag{5b}$$
$$n + p \nrightarrow n + n + p \tag{5c}$$
$$n + p \nrightarrow n + p + p + \pi^- \tag{5d}$$

Why don't these reactions occur? The question can be answered by using the concept of **baryon number**, a property that is somewhat analogous to charge. It is found that in order to explain why certain interactions appear to be forbidden it is necessary to assume that:

(i) Each hadron has an associated value of baryon number B (some examples are given in Table 4);

TABLE 4   Baryon numbers of some hadrons

Hadron	Baryon number B
p	1
n	1
π^-	0
π^0	0
π^+	0

(ii) Each lepton and gauge boson (to be discussed later) has baryon number zero;

(iii) The total baryon number of all the hadrons *before* a strong interaction is equal to the total baryon number of the hadrons *after* the interaction—baryon number is conserved.

The baryon number of the proton is defined to be $+1$, and from this definition a unique value for the baryon number of every other particle can be deduced by assuming that baryon number is conserved in every strong interaction. For example, if a single new particle C is produced in a collision between two protons, it follows from baryon number conservation that the baryon number of C is zero:

$$p + p \rightarrow p + p + C \qquad \text{observed}$$
$$B \quad \underbrace{1 \quad 1}_{2} \quad \underbrace{1 \quad 1 \quad 0}_{= \quad 2} \qquad B \text{ conserved}$$

Particle C should then have this same value of baryon number $B = 0$ *in all other interactions*.

What makes the idea of baryon number so useful is the experimentally observed fact that one can ascribe a *unique* value of baryon number to every hadron—once the value of a hadron's baryon number has been determined in one interaction, the same value can be used in all other interactions. This allows us to predict whether an interaction will or will not occur. Remember, only reactions in which baryon number is conserved are observed in practice.

Baryon number conservation easily explains why the four strong interactions 5a–5d do *not* occur. In each of them, baryon number is *not* conserved:

$$p + p \nrightarrow p + p + n \qquad \text{not observed} \qquad (5a)*$$
$$B \quad \underbrace{1 \quad 1}_{2} \quad \underbrace{1 \quad 1 \quad 1}_{\neq \quad 3} \qquad B \text{ not conserved}$$

$$p + p \nrightarrow p + p + n + n \qquad \text{not observed} \qquad (5b)*$$
$$B \quad \underbrace{1 \quad 1}_{2} \quad \underbrace{1 \quad 1 \quad 1 \quad 1}_{\neq \quad 4} \qquad B \text{ not conserved}$$

$$n + p \nrightarrow n + n + p \qquad \text{not observed} \qquad (5c)*$$
$$B \quad \underbrace{1 \quad 1}_{2} \quad \underbrace{1 \quad 1 \quad 1}_{\neq \quad 3} \qquad B \text{ not conserved}$$

$$n + p \nrightarrow n + p + p + \pi^- \qquad \text{not observed} \qquad (5d)*$$
$$B \quad \underbrace{1 \quad 1}_{2} \quad \underbrace{1 \quad 1 \quad 1 \quad 0}_{\neq \quad 3} \qquad B \text{ not conserved}$$

It is worth stressing that in every reaction baryon number and charge are *both* conserved. If you write down a reaction in which *either* of the two properties is not conserved, you can be sure that the reaction has not been observed.

ITQ 4 Which one of the following reactions is forbidden because either charge or baryon number (or both) is not conserved? (Refer to Table 4.)

(a) $p + p \rightarrow \pi^+ + p + n$

(b) $p + p \rightarrow \pi^+ + p + n + n$

(c) $p + p \rightarrow p + p + \pi^0 + \pi^0$

MESON

BARYON

STRANGENESS

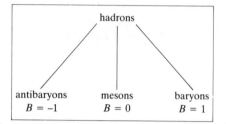

FIGURE 21 Each hadron observed to date can be classified as either an antibaryon ($B = -1$), a meson ($B = 0$) or a baryon ($B = 1$).

It is useful to classify hadrons into three types (Figure 21): those with zero baryon number, the **mesons**; those with baryon number one, the **baryons**; and those with baryon number minus one, the antibaryons. Hence the proton and neutron (p and n) are baryons and the π^-, π^0 and π^+ are mesons.

It was once believed that baryons are generally heavier than mesons (the word baryon is derived from the Greek word *barus* meaning heavy). However, recent experiments have shown that some mesons are heavier than some baryons, as you will see in Section 6.

4.2.3 STRANGENESS AND ITS CONSERVATION

In the mid-1950s another property of hadrons was postulated by the American theoretical physicist Murray Gell-Mann and (independently) by the Japanese theoretical physicist Kazuhiko Nishijima. This property was called **strangeness** by Gell-Mann, who subsequently introduced several other whimsical terms into the vocabulary of particle physics, as you will see later.

The strangeness S of a hadron may be introduced in exactly the same way as charge Q and baryon number B were introduced:

(i) Each hadron has an associated value of strangeness S.

(ii) Each lepton and gauge boson has zero strangeness.

(iii) The total strangeness of all the hadrons before a strong interaction is equal to the total strangeness of the hadrons after the interaction; in other words, strangeness is conserved in strong interactions.

By defining the strangeness of the K^+ particle to be $+1$ and by applying strangeness conservation to strong interactions that have been observed, it is possible to assign to each hadron a unique value of strangeness. This procedure is of course precisely analogous to the ones used earlier to ascribe a value of charge and baryon number to particles. (Remember, the charge and baryon number of the proton are each defined to be $+1$.)

The values of Q, B and S for the hadrons in Figure 19 are given, with their names and rest masses, in Table 5. (There is no need for you to remember the contents of this Table.)

TABLE 5 Some assorted hadrons (in alphabetical order)

Name	Symbol	Rest mass /(GeV/c^2)	Q	B	S
delta minus	Δ^-	1.232	-1	1	0
delta plus	Δ^+	1.232	1	1	0
delta plus plus	Δ^{++}	1.232	2	1	0
delta zero	Δ^0	1.232	0	1	0
K minus	K^-	0.4937	-1	0	-1
K plus	K^+	0.4937	1	0	1
K zero	K^0	0.4977	0	0	1
K zero bar	$\bar{K}^0$	0.4977	0	0	-1
lambda	Λ	1.116	0	1	-1
neutron	n	0.9396	0	1	0
phi	ϕ	1.020	0	0	0
pi minus	π^-	0.1396	-1	0	0
pi plus	π^+	0.1396	1	0	0
pi zero	π^0	0.1350	0	0	0
proton	p	0.9383	1	1	0
sigma minus	Σ^-	1.197	-1	1	-1
sigma plus	Σ^+	1.189	1	1	-1
sigma zero	Σ^0	1.192	0	1	-1
xi minus	Ξ^-	1.315	-1	1	-2
xi zero	Ξ^0	1.321	0	1	-2

In this Table, each value of rest mass is quoted to four significant figures and each value of charge is given in units of the charge e of the proton.

The introduction of strangeness enables an understanding of why the strong interactions 6a–6d do occur, while the strong interactions 7a–7d do not. In all of the interactions, charge and baryon number are conserved, but only in the interactions 6a–6d is strangeness conserved.

$$\pi^- + p \rightarrow K^+ + \Sigma^- \tag{6a}$$

$$S \quad \underbrace{0 \quad 0} \quad \underbrace{1 \quad -1}$$

$$0 \quad = \quad 0 \qquad S \text{ conserved}$$

$$\pi^+ + n \rightarrow K^+ + \Sigma^0 \tag{6b}$$

$$S \quad \underbrace{0 \quad 0} \quad \underbrace{1 \quad -1}$$

$$0 \quad = \quad 0 \qquad S \text{ conserved}$$

$$K^- + p \rightarrow \pi^+ + \Sigma^- \tag{6c}$$

$$S \quad \underbrace{-1 \quad 0} \quad \underbrace{0 \quad -1}$$

$$-1 \quad = \quad -1 \qquad S \text{ conserved}$$

$$K^- + p \rightarrow K^+ + \Xi^- \tag{6d}$$

$$S \quad \underbrace{-1 + 0} \quad \underbrace{1 \quad -2}$$

$$-1 \quad = \quad -1 \qquad S \text{ conserved}$$

$$\pi^- + p \nrightarrow K^- + \Sigma^+ \tag{7a}$$

$$S \quad \underbrace{0 \quad 0} \quad \underbrace{-1 \quad -1}$$

$$0 \quad \neq \quad -2 \qquad S \text{ not conserved}$$

$$\pi^+ + n \nrightarrow \pi^+ + \Lambda \tag{7b}$$

$$S \quad \underbrace{0 \quad 0} \quad \underbrace{0 \quad -1}$$

$$0 \quad \neq \quad -1 \qquad S \text{ not conserved}$$

$$K^+ + p \nrightarrow \pi^+ + \Sigma^+ \tag{7c}$$

$$S \quad \underbrace{1 \quad 0} \quad \underbrace{0 \quad -1}$$

$$1 \quad \neq \quad -1 \qquad S \text{ not conserved}$$

$$K^- + p \nrightarrow \pi^+ + \Xi^- \tag{7d}$$

$$S \quad \underbrace{-1 \quad 0} \quad \underbrace{0 \quad -2}$$

$$-1 \quad \neq \quad -2 \qquad S \text{ not conserved}$$

By now you may be feeling bewildered by the number of hadrons that you've met in this Section, not to mention the conserved intrinsic properties that have been introduced. Try not to be overwhelmed—the most important point that you need to grasp is that of all the millions of strong interactions that might be predicted to occur, it is found experimentally that the only reactions that are actually observed are those in which charge Q, baryon number B and strangeness S are each conserved. The associated conservation laws tell us which strong interactions will occur and which will not.

What is the physical 'meaning' of baryon number and strangeness? In other words, what is meant by the statement that a hadron has a certain baryon number B and a certain strangeness S? This question is answered similarly to the way in which the question 'What is the meaning of charge?' was answered at the end of Section 4.1. When a hadron is said to have certain values of B and S, statements are implicitly being made about the effect the hadron can have on other particles. The values are labels that allow predictions to be made about whether reactions that involve the hadron are forbidden or not; you have seen several examples of such predictions in this Section.

Finally, we ought to point out that, whereas charge and baryon number are conserved in *all* interactions, strangeness is conserved only in strong and electromagnetic interactions but *not* in weak interactions. There is no need for you to be concerned about this point in this Course.

SAQ 7 By checking to see whether Q, B and S are each conserved, decide which one of the strong interactions (a)–(c) can occur.

(a) $\pi^- + p \rightarrow n + p$

(b) $\Sigma^- + p \rightarrow K^0 + n$

(c) $K^- + p \rightarrow \bar{K}^0 + n$

SAQ 8 The following strong interaction was first observed in 1964 at the Brookhaven laboratory in the USA:

$$K^- + p \rightarrow K^0 + K^+ + X$$

where X is a hadron that had, until then, not be observed.

(a) What is the charge of X, in units of *coulombs*?

(b) Is X a meson or a baryon?

(c) What is the strangeness of X?

4.3 ARE HADRONS FUNDAMENTAL PARTICLES?

You have seen in this Section that hundreds of hadrons have been observed. Are they all fundamental particles, or do they have constituents? This question was addressed in the late 1960s in some crucial experiments that were done at SLAC, in California. These experiments are closely analogous to one carried out at Manchester University by Rutherford's collaborators more than 60 years before, in order to probe the structure of the *atom*.

Before we consider the SLAC experiments, it is worthwhile to revise briefly the Manchester experiment, which was first discussed in Units 11–12. In this experiment, α-particles (with a de Broglie wavelength of approximately 10^{-15} m) were directed towards a target of gold foil, in order to investigate the structure of the atoms in the target. At the time of the experiment, it was widely believed that the equal amount of positive and negative charge in each atom are both distributed *uniformly*. Calculations based on this idea led to the firm expectation that almost all of the α-particles would pass practically unperturbed through each gold atom (Figure 22a). However, it was found, to the amazement of Ernest Rutherford, that a significant proportion of the incident α-particles were scattered at large angles (see Figure 22b, which bears more than a passing resemblance to the cover of Units 11–12). Rutherford brilliantly used this result to suggest that the positive charge of the atom is concentrated in a tiny core, which he called the nucleus.

The α-scattering experiment therefore enabled the structure of the atom to be probed. The team of experimenters at SLAC used a similar type of experiment to probe the structure of *nuclear* constituents—protons and neutrons.

The team used beams of electrons with energies of approximately 6 GeV, and a corresponding de Broglie wavelength of approximately 10^{-16} m. Note that the wavelength required to probe the contents of a proton or neutron is smaller than the wavelength of approximately 10^{-15} m used in the Manchester experiment to probe the atom. (The wavelengths reflect the sizes of the entities under investigation as you saw in Section 2.)

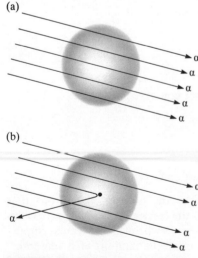

(a)

(b)

FIGURE 22 Before the α-scattering experiment was done, it was expected that nearly all of the incident α-particles would pass straight through the gold atoms (a), because the atoms were believed to consist of *uniform* distributions of positive and negative charge. However, it was found that a surprisingly high proportion of the α-particles were scattered at large angles (b), and this led Rutherford to suggest (correctly) that atoms each have a nucleus in which their positive charge is concentrated.

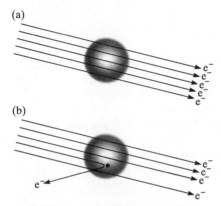

FIGURE 23 The SLAC experiments showed that a surprisingly high proportion of incident electrons are scattered at large angles from protons and neutrons. This evidence supported the idea that protons and neutrons have point-like, charged constituents.

Before the SLAC experiments were done, some physicists visualized the proton and neutron (and other hadrons) as jelly-like particles, with their masses distributed over regions of approximately 10^{-15} m in diameter. In such a visualization, the *charge* of the proton is also distributed over the region that the particle occupies. (The neutron of course has no charge.)

If this picture were correct, the overwhelming majority of the high-energy electrons incident on a proton or neutron would pass through practically unperturbed (Figure 23a). However, the experimenters at SLAC found that a significant proportion of the electrons were scattered through large angles (Figure 23b). Careful interpretations of these data, notably by the American theoretical physicist Richard Feynman, showed that the results of the electron-scattering experiments indicated that *protons and neutrons contain point-like, charged constituents.* This idea was later confirmed by experiments in which protons and neutrons were bombarded by other leptons, and by antileptons.

Because the proton and neutron are in many respects typical hadrons, it was reasonable to extend the conclusion of the Stanford experiments:

> Hadrons are *not* fundamental particles—they *contain* other particles with charge that do appear to be fundamental.

The charged fundamental particles of which hadrons are made will be discussed in the next Section.

SUMMARY OF SECTION 4

1 Hadrons are particles that feel the strong interaction (the interaction that is responsible for the binding together of protons and neutrons in nuclei).

2 Each hadron has an associated value of charge Q, baryon number B and strangeness S.

3 Hadrons that have zero baryon number are known as mesons, those that have baryon number one are known as baryons, and those that have baryon number minus one are known as antibaryons.

4 Charge and baryon number are conserved in all interactions.

5 Strangeness is conserved in strong and electromagnetic interactions but not in weak interactions.

6 Hadrons are not fundamental particles.

SAQ 9   Which of the following types of particle (a)–(c) is currently believed to be fundamental and which are subject to strong interactions? (a) Mesons; (b) baryons; (c) leptons.

5 QUARKS

Several years before the SLAC scattering experiments were performed, it had been suggested that hadrons have fundamental constituents—quarks, and their antiparticles, antiquarks. In this Section, we shall introduce these constituents and show how, according to the simple quark model of hadrons, the charge Q, baryon number B and strangeness S of each hadron are determined by the values of Q, B and S of its constituent quarks and antiquarks. The Section will be concluded by a brief discussion of the interactions of these fundamental hadronic constituents.

QUARK

SIMPLE QUARK MODEL

FIGURE 24   Murray Gell-Mann received the 1969 Nobel Prize in physics for 'his contributions and discoveries concerning the classification of elementary particles and their interactions'. Gell-Mann was involved in many of the important steps forward in theoretical particle physics, notably the discovery of the property of strangeness, the formulation of laws concerning the weak interaction, the identification of patterns among the properties of hadrons, and the formulation of the theory of quantum chromodynamics (Section 5.2).

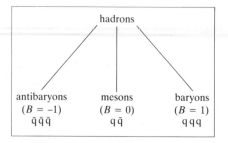

FIGURE 25   Every known hadron can, according to the simple quark model, be interpreted as a combination (with $B = -1$) of three antiquarks, as a combination (with $B = 0$) of a quark and an antiquark or as a combination (with $B = 1$) of three quarks.

5.1 THREE QUARKS AND THEIR ANTIPARTICLES

The idea that hadrons might have fundamental constituents was introduced in 1964 by Murray Gell-Mann (Figure 24) and, independently, by George Zweig. They identified three basic varieties of the constituents, and this led Gell-Mann to call them collectively **quarks**, a reference to the phrase 'Three quarks for Muster Mark!' which occurs in *Finnegan's Wake*, the eccentrically written novel by James Joyce. The word quark has two conventional pronunciations—in one it rhymes with shark, in the other it rhymes with pork. Physicists choose their favoured pronunciation according to taste.

Gell-Mann called the three quarks 'up', 'down' and 'strange' and he denoted them by u, d and s, respectively. As you can see in Table 6, each of these varieties of quark—and their corresponding antiparticles, antiquarks—has a characteristic charge Q, baryon number B, strangeness S and a rest mass that can, however, be given only *approximately* (we shall return to this subject later). Note from Table 6 that, for each variety of quark, its values of Q, B and S are opposite to that of the corresponding antiquark, whereas its rest mass is the same as that of its antiquark. This is just as you should expect from the definition of an antiparticle (Section 3).

TABLE 6   Properties of u, d and s quarks, and of the corresponding antiquarks, ū, d̄ and s̄

	Charge Q	Baryon number B	Strangeness S	Approximate rest mass/ (GeV/c^2)
u	$+\frac{2}{3}$	$+\frac{1}{3}$	0	0.005
d	$-\frac{1}{3}$	$+\frac{1}{3}$	0	0.01
s	$-\frac{1}{3}$	$+\frac{1}{3}$	-1	0.2
ū	$-\frac{2}{3}$	$-\frac{1}{3}$	0	0.005
d̄	$+\frac{1}{3}$	$-\frac{1}{3}$	0	0.01
s̄	$+\frac{1}{3}$	$-\frac{1}{3}$	$+1$	0.2

According to the **simple quark model** of hadrons, each baryon, antibaryon and meson consists of a certain combination of quarks and antiquarks (Figure 25):

(i) Each baryon (i.e. hadron with baryon number 1) consists of three quarks, which may or may not be of the same variety.

(ii) Each meson (i.e. hadron with zero baryon number) consists of a quark and an antiquark, which may or may not be of the same variety.

(iii) Each antibaryon, (i.e. hadron with baryon number -1) consists of three antiquarks, which may or may not be of the same variety.

The charge of each hadron is simply equal to the *sum* of the charges of its constituent quarks and antiquarks, and the same goes for its baryon number and strangeness.

Consider, for example, the proton, which has charge $+1$, baryon number $+1$ and strangeness 0 (Table 5). These properties are easily accounted for by assuming that the proton consists of two u quarks and one d quark (refer to Table 6 to check the values of Q, B and S for the quarks):

$$p = u \quad u \quad d$$
$$Q \quad 1 = \tfrac{2}{3} + \tfrac{2}{3} - \tfrac{1}{3}$$
$$B \quad 1 = \tfrac{1}{3} + \tfrac{1}{3} + \tfrac{1}{3}$$
$$S \quad 0 = 0 + 0 + 0$$

The corresponding properties of the neutron can also be easily understood if it is assumed to consist of one u quark and two d quarks:

$$n = u \quad d \quad d$$

$$Q \quad 0 = \tfrac{2}{3} - \tfrac{1}{3} - \tfrac{1}{3}$$

$$B \quad 1 = \tfrac{1}{3} + \tfrac{1}{3} + \tfrac{1}{3}$$

$$S \quad 0 = 0 + 0 + 0$$

As two final examples, consider the K^+ and its antiparticle, the K^- (Table 5). The properties of these mesons (which have strangeness $S = +1$ and $S = -1$ respectively) are easily accounted for if they are assumed to be the following quark–antiquark combinations:

$$K^+ = u \quad \bar{s} \qquad\qquad K^- = \bar{u} \quad s$$

$$Q \quad 1 = \tfrac{2}{3} + \tfrac{1}{3} \qquad Q \quad -1 = -\tfrac{2}{3} - \tfrac{1}{3}$$

$$B \quad 0 = \tfrac{1}{3} - \tfrac{1}{3} \qquad B \quad 0 = -\tfrac{1}{3} + \tfrac{1}{3}$$

$$S \quad 1 = 0 + 1 \qquad S \quad -1 = 0 - 1$$

The simple quark model is not only easy to apply, it is also extremely powerful—the properties of every hadron that has ever been observed can be understood respectively in terms of a three-quark, a three-antiquark or a quark–antiquark combination. Some examples of these combinations (including the ones already discussed here) are collected together for easy reference in Table 7.

Perhaps the most appealing feature of the simple quark model is the remarkable simplification that it introduces into the physics of hadrons. The model enabled the bewildering (and increasing) number of hadrons to be understood in terms of only a few constituents and their antiparticles. You might think that because hadrons can be made from only a small number of varieties of quark, the number of hadrons that can exist should be strictly limited by the possible number of three-quark, three-antiquark and quark-antiquark combinations. However, there is no such limitation, for hadrons with *different* rest masses but with the *same* values of Q, B and S can be made from *the same* combination of quarks and antiquarks. For example, two u quarks and an s quark can form a Σ^+ baryon, with rest mass $1.189\,\mathrm{GeV}/c^2$, or a Σ^{*+} baryon, with rest mass $1.383\,\mathrm{GeV}/c^2$. The Σ^{*+} is merely an excited state of the three quarks:[†] it has the same charge, baryon number and strangeness as the Σ^+; but the rest mass of the Σ^{*+} is higher than that of the Σ^+, because the energy of the uus combination is higher in the Σ^{*+} than it is in the Σ^+.

When the simple quark model was suggested, it was clear that the model allowed the charge, baryon number and strangeness of many hadrons to be understood easily. However, the model did have many problems. For example, it certainly could not explain all the experimental observations of the interactions that hadrons undergo. More important, *neither a quark nor an antiquark had been observed in isolation.* Hence, proponents of the model were forced to assume that, for some reason, *quarks and antiquarks can exist only inside hadrons.* To many physicists, this assumption was highly improbable—if hadrons really do contain quarks and antiquarks, why aren't these constituents liberated when hadrons collide at high energies?

TABLE 7 Constituents of some hadrons (baryons and mesons), according to the simple quark model

Hadron	Constituents
p	uud
n	udd
Δ^-	ddd
Δ^0	udd
Δ^+	uud
Δ^{++}	uuu
Λ	uds
Σ^-	dds
Σ^0	uds
Σ^+	uus
Ξ^-	dss
Ξ^0	uss
π^+	$u\bar{d}$
π^-	$\bar{u}d$
π^0	$u\bar{u}$ or $d\bar{d}$
K^+	$u\bar{s}$
K^-	$\bar{u}s$
K^0	$d\bar{s}$
$\overline{K}^0$	$\bar{d}s$
ϕ	$s\bar{s}$

[†] You have met this phenomenon before in atomic and nuclear physics. For example, a hydrogen atom consists of an electron and a proton, but it can exist in states of different energy (Units 11–12 and 31). Similarly, atomic nuclei can exist in excited states (Unit 31).

STRONG INTERACTION BETWEEN QUARKS

QUANTUM CHROMODYNAMICS

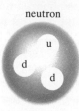

FIGURE 26   According to the simple quark model, a proton consists of two u quarks and one d quark (p = uud) and a neutron consists of one u quark and two d quarks (n = udd).

Bearing in mind these problems, it is perhaps not surprising that the simple quark model was first received by particle physicists with considerable scepticism. Zweig, one of the proponents of the model, has written:

> Getting the CERN report [in which I first put forward the quark model] published was so difficult that I finally gave up trying. When the physics department of a leading University was considering an appointment for me, their senior theorist, one of the most respected spokesmen for all theoretical physics, blocked the appointment at a faculty meeting by passionately arguing that the [quark] model was the work of a 'charlatan'.

To this day, isolated quarks and isolated antiquarks have still not been observed. It is therefore not possible to measure directly their rest masses. Indeed, it is not possible to deduce from the rest masses of hadrons the rest masses of the quarks that they contain. Similarly, it is not possible to calculate the rest mass of a hadron simply by adding the rest masses of the constituents. You can easily check that this is true for each hadron in Table 7, using the data in Tables 5 and 6. For example the rest mass of the proton is $0.9383 \, \text{GeV}/c^2$, whereas the total rest mass of its constituent u and d quarks is only $(0.005 + 0.005 + 0.01) \, \text{GeV}/c^2 = 0.02 \, \text{GeV}/c^2$.

Ever since the quark model was formulated, the problem of understanding the rest masses of quarks has been an important area of research in theoretical particle physics. Although it is not possible to give precise values for these masses, the values can be quoted approximately. But do remember that the values of the rest masses of quarks that we give are subject to change!

About six years elapsed after Gell-Mann and Zweig's proposal of the idea of quarks and antiquarks before the scientific community accepted that quarks and antiquarks really do exist in hadrons. Some of the most compelling evidence for their existence came from the SLAC experiments, which were described in Section 4. It was found that the data from these (and other) experiments could be easily understood if each proton contains two fundamental particles with charge $+\frac{2}{3}$ and one with charge $-\frac{1}{3}$, and if each neutron contains one fundamental particle with charge $+\frac{2}{3}$ and two with charge $-\frac{1}{3}$ (Figure 26). This, of course, is beautifully in accord with the simple quark model (p = uud, n = udd).

But why are isolated quarks (and antiquarks) not observed? That question was addressed successfully in the 1970s by theories of quark and antiquark interactions. We shall consider these interactions next.

5.2 THE INTERACTIONS OF QUARKS AND ANTIQUARKS

In common with all electrically charged fundamental particles and antiparticles, quarks and antiquarks have gravitational and electromagnetic interactions. They can also interact weakly, and it is their weak interaction that is responsible for the basic process of β-decay of nuclei (Unit 31). Consider, for example, the basic process of β^--decay:

$$n \rightarrow p + e^- + \bar{\nu}_e$$

which is illustrated schematically in Figure 27. As you can see, in this process a d quark (in the neutron) transmutes into a u quark (in the proton), with the ejection of an electron and electron antineutrino. The laws that describe this transmutation are the same as those that describe the weak interactions of leptons.

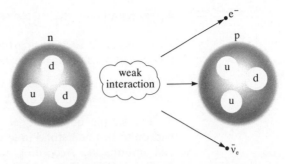

FIGURE 27 At a fundamental level, the β^- decay of a neutron into a proton, an electron and an electron antineutrino $\bar{\nu}_e$ occurs owing to a weak interaction in which a d quark transmutes into a u quark with the emission of an electron and an electron antineutrino $(d \to u + e^- + \bar{\nu}_e)$.

The binding together of quarks (in a baryon), antiquarks (in an antibaryon) and quark–antiquark pairs (in a meson) is due to their *strong* interactions. These interactions really are very strong: the magnitude of the force between two quarks separated by 10^{-15} m is approximately 100 000 N, equivalent to the weight on Earth of ten tonnes (10^4 kg)! Also, these interactions are of very short range, approximately 10^{-15} m.

The **strong interaction between quarks** is responsible for the binding of protons and neutrons in atomic nuclei. Each proton and neutron contains quarks that are bound together, and there is a *residual* strong interaction between the protons and neutrons themselves (Figure 28). This residual interaction between protons and neutrons in an atomic nucleus is typical of the strong interaction between hadrons which you met in Section 4, where hadronic collisions were discussed. However, it is important to note that the strong interactions between hadrons are *not* fundamental. (Remember from Section 1 that a fundamental interaction by definition cannot be understood theoretically in terms of a more basic interaction.) It is the strong interaction between the constituent quarks and antiquarks of hadrons that is believed to be truly fundamental: the strong interactions between hadrons are residual to the interactions between their constituent quarks and antiquarks.

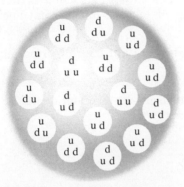

FIGURE 28 A typical nucleus consists of protons and neutrons which, according to the simple quark model, consist of u and d quarks. The interaction between the quarks is believed to be fundamental—it cannot currently be understood in terms of a more basic interaction.

In Table 8, the strength and range of the strong interaction between quarks (and antiquarks) are compared with those of the other three fundamental interactions—electromagnetic, weak and gravitational. This Table shows that the strong interaction is considerably stronger than the other types of fundamental interaction.

The best available theoretical description of the fundamental strong interaction is given by **quantum chromodynamics**, a theory that was formulated in the early 1970s. According to quantum chromodynamics (usually abbreviated to QCD), each particle that participates in fundamental strong interactions has the property 'colour' (hence *chromo*). This property, which has nothing to do with the conventional meaning of colour, plays a role in strong interactions that is analogous to the role played by electrical charge in electromagnetic interactions. Incidentally, it was Gell-Mann who coined the terms quantum chromodynamics and 'colour'.

TABLE 8 Ranges and relative strengths of the four fundamental interactions (order of magnitude estimates)

Type	Range/m	Relative strength*
strong	10^{-15}	10^2
electromagnetic	∞	1
weak	10^{-18}	10^{-3}
gravitational	∞	10^{-36}

* These strengths refer to interactions probed using an energy of 1 GeV. (See the footnote to Table 2 in Section 3.)

The QCD theory is extremely complex, so much so that it is difficult in many cases to make detailed predictions about the behaviour of quarks and antiquarks. For example, it is extremely difficult to predict the behaviour of quarks and antiquarks at comparatively large separations (greater than, say, 10^{-14} m). The theory has, however, led physicists to expect that isolated quarks and isolated antiquarks will not be detected, an expectation that (as you saw earlier) is currently in agreement with observation.

If individual quarks and antiquarks were ever detected in isolation, the impact on particle physics would be very considerable, to say the least. Such a discovery would cause theorists to modify their basic ideas of the fundamental strong interaction, and the theory of quantum chromodynamics would almost certainly have to be radically revised. Such disarray among theorists would be a rich prize for experimenters!

LEPTON–QUARK
SYMMETRY

CHARM

SUMMARY OF SECTION 5

1 Quarks and their antiparticles (antiquarks) are currently believed to be fundamental, i.e. to have no constituents.

2 When the idea of quarks was first put forward, it was suggested that there were three types of quark—up (u), down (d) and strange (s).

3 The simple quark model of hadrons enables the properties of each hadron to be understood in terms of the properties of its constituent quarks and antiquarks. According to the model, each baryon contains three quarks, each antibaryon contains three antiquarks and each meson contains a quark and an antiquark.

4 Quarks (and antiquarks) each have electromagnetic, weak and gravitational interactions, but it is their strong interactions that are responsible for their being bound together as hadrons. The strong interaction between quarks and antiquarks is currently believed to be a fundamental interaction.

5 Isolated quarks and isolated antiquarks have not been observed and, according to current theoretical ideas, they never will be.

SAQ 10 Which two of the following statements (a)–(e) about quarks and antiquarks are currently believed to be correct?

(a) They have no constituents.

(b) They exist in leptons.

(c) They exist in hadrons.

(d) The only fundamental interaction to which they are subject is the strong interaction.

(e) Their tracks have been observed in drift chambers.

SAQ 11 What is the overall charge, baryon number and strangeness of the hadrons that, according to the simple quark model, have the following constituents? (a) uss; (b) ud̄. (Hint: Refer to Table 6.)

6 THE LEPTON–QUARK SYMMETRY

So far, you have met two types of fundamental particle—leptons and quarks—each of which comes in several varieties. The number of varieties of lepton can actually be linked to the number of varieties of quark by the **lepton–quark symmetry**, according to which

> The number of pairs of leptons (one with charge -1, the other with charge 0) is equal to the number of pairs of quarks (one with charge $+\frac{2}{3}$, the other with charge $-\frac{1}{3}$).

This symmetry implies that *the number of varieties of lepton is equal to the number of varieties of quark*. The equality of the two numbers is not only aesthetically pleasing, it also has profound theoretical implications: it was realized in the early 1970s that the lepton–quark symmetry is essential in order to ensure that the widely accepted (and very successful) theory of weak and electromagnetic interactions (Section 7) is physically reasonable. If the symmetry did not exist, then the theory would have to be considerably modified!

We shall show in this Section that the lepton–quark symmetry enabled four new varieties of fundamental particle to be predicted, and we shall compare these predictions with experiment in order to check their validity. You will see in following this discussion that it has proved necessary to introduce some new intrinsic properties of hadrons, notably 'charm'.

6.1 PHYSICISTS DISCOVER CHARM

You have already seen that the four leptons that you met in Section 3—the electron e^-, the mu minus μ^- and their associated neutrinos ν_e and ν_μ—can be grouped together:

$$\begin{pmatrix} e^- & \mu^- \\ \nu_e & \nu_\mu \end{pmatrix} \begin{array}{l} \leftarrow & Q = -1 \\ \leftarrow & Q = 0 \end{array}$$

where we have indicated the charge Q of the particles in each of the two horizontal rows. Also, you have just seen in Section 5 that Gell-Mann and Zweig proposed the existence of *three* quarks—u, d and s. These fundamental particles can also be grouped together:

$$\begin{pmatrix} u & \\ d & s \end{pmatrix} \begin{array}{l} \leftarrow & Q = +\tfrac{2}{3} \\ \leftarrow & Q = -\tfrac{1}{3} \end{array}$$

It is easy to see that, in order to ensure that there is a lepton–quark symmetry, there should exist another quark that has charge $+\tfrac{2}{3}$. The existence of such a fourth quark was first suggested (two years before the idea of the lepton–quark symmetry was put forward!) by the American physicist Sheldon Lee Glashow and his European collaborators John Iliopoulos and Luciano Maiani. They suggested, on the basis of a number of complex theoretical arguments, that the new quark should have a property that is analogous to strangeness in the sense that it should be conserved in strong and electromagnetic interactions, but not in weak interactions. This property is called **charm**, and the new quark is therefore referred to as the c quark. In Table 9, its predicted properties are compared with the corresponding properties of the u, d and s quarks.

TABLE 9 Properties of the u, d and s quarks, and the predicted properties of the c quark

Type of quark	Charge Q	Baryon number B	Strangeness S	Charm C	Approximate rest mass $/(\text{GeV}/c^2)$
u	$+\tfrac{2}{3}$	$+\tfrac{1}{3}$	0	0	0.005
d	$-\tfrac{1}{3}$	$+\tfrac{1}{3}$	0	0	0.01
s	$-\tfrac{1}{3}$	$+\tfrac{1}{3}$	-1	0	0.2
c	$+\tfrac{2}{3}$	$+\tfrac{1}{3}$	0	1	1.5

ITQ 5 Refer to Table 9. What were the predicted values of the charge, baryon number, strangeness, charm and rest mass of the $\bar{c}$ antiquark?

The symmetry between the four quarks and the four leptons

$$\begin{pmatrix} u & c \\ d & s \end{pmatrix} \qquad \begin{pmatrix} e^- & \mu^- \\ \nu_e & \nu_\mu \end{pmatrix}$$

is appealing (and theoretically essential), but it could not be said to have been realized in nature until the existence of the c quark had been confirmed *experimentally*.

Ten years after the new quark was postulated, there was no evidence whatsoever for hadrons that appeared to contain it. However, in the early 1970s, most particle physicists became increasingly convinced that charm (an essential ingredient in their theories of the fundamental interactions) would be observed. A group of theoreticians was even able to predict that charmed hadrons would be observed with rest masses around $3\,\text{GeV}/c^2$. However, there was considerable debate about which type of reaction would give experimenters the best chance of finding these particles.

By the autumn of 1974, the idea of charm was well established in theoretical terms, but it had no direct support from the results of experiments. Then, on 11 November 1974, a remarkable announcement came from the USA.

Two teams of experimenters, one working at SLAC in California, the other at the Brookhaven accelerator near New York, reported that they had independently observed a new particle with truly extraordinary properties. Its rest mass, approximately $3.1\,\text{GeV}/c^2$, was greater than that of any other particle, and it lived about 2 000 times as long as most hadrons!

The Brookhaven team (Figure 29) discovered the particle, which they called the J, in a fixed-target experiment that involved the collision of high-energy protons with the nuclei in a stationary beryllium target. Three thousand miles away, the SLAC team (Figure 30) discovered the particle, which they called the ψ (pronounced psi, rhyming with eye), in a colliding-beam experiment in which electrons collide with positrons in an electronic detector (Figure 31). In order to avoid giving the particle two names, J and ψ, it is usually called the J/ψ (pronounced jay-psi or, sometimes, gypsy!)

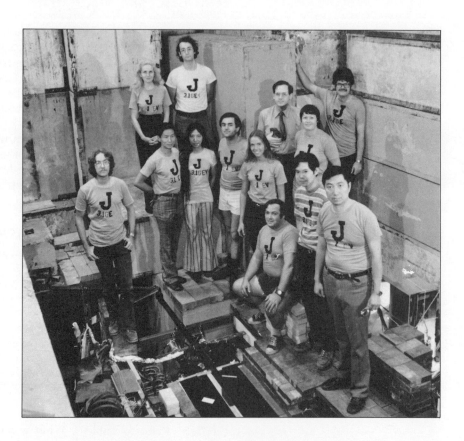

FIGURE 29   Samuel Ting (at the bottom of the photograph on the far right) and the team of physicists (from the Massachusetts Institute of Technology) that discovered the J/ψ at the Brookhaven laboratory.

Ten days later, the SLAC team discovered in their e^+e^- experiment another heavy, electrically neutral particle, the ψ' (pronounced psi prime), with a rest mass of approximately $3.695\,\text{GeV}/c^2$. The team subsequently went on to study in detail the properties of the new particles. They found that the ψ and the ψ' are both mesons (hadrons with zero baryon number) with zero strangeness and zero charm. These properties were subsequently confirmed by experimenters at other accelerators.

The discovery of the new particles, particularly the J/ψ, caused pandemonium among high-energy physicists, who now refer to this dramatic phase in the development of their subject as the November Revolution. News of the upheaval even spread to the world outside (Figure 32)!

The central question that had to be answered was: How can the extraordinary properties of the new particles be understood? This problem was addressed in hundreds of scientific papers, many of which involved hurriedly formulated theories and ideas that now appear to be somewhat bizarre. For example, it was suggested that the J/ψ could be a gauge boson or a hitherto undetected type of particle that consists of a baryon–antibaryon pair. Although these ideas were plausible when they were proposed (a few days after the J/ψ was discovered), physicists soon discarded them when it was realized that their predictions did not agree with experiment.

Physicists excited over new particle

Stanford, California, Nov. 17.—American physicists yesterday announced the discovery of a new kind of elementary particle—a basic constituent of all matter—with hitherto unknown properties.

The discovery was made independently by scientific teams at Stanford University's linear accelerator centre and the Brookhaven National Laboratory in New York.

In an announcement made simultaneously by both laboratories, Mr Burton Richter, of the Stanford team, and Mr Samuel C. C. Ting, of the Brookhaven team, said: " The suddenness of the discovery, coupled with the totally unexpected properties of the particle are what make it so exciting. It is not like the particles we know and must have some new kind of structure."

The researchers said that they did not yet fully understand the discovery but it might fill in some spaces in the physical knowledge of the universe. " The discovery is abstract. We do not know what it means ", they said. Theorists were " working frantically " to fit the discovery into the framework of present knowledge.

Elementary particles, so small that they cannot be seen under a microscope, make up all matter and energy.

It has long been known that atoms are composed of three fundamental, or elementary, particles—the protons and neutrons making up the core of atoms, and the electrons circling them somewhat like the planets orbiting the sun.

The new particle, which has been given the name Psi, is said to have hitherto unknown properties.

According to Mr Richter, the Psi particle is " different from all the other particles we know. It lives 100,000 times longer than any other particle, and therefore must have a new kind of structure of holding it together ".

One physicist said the existence of the particle may eventually explain many discrepancies in fundamental physical theories. Another scientist said : " This is one of the biggest discoveries in high energy physics in years anywhere in the world."

Both the Stanford and Brookhaven groups said the new particle occurred at an energy of just over three billion electron volts.

They said the particle decays into other heavy particles, called hadrons or leptons, in one hundred billionth of a billionth of a second. On a nuclear time scale this is a remarkably long life.

Both laboratories made their discoveries while conducting research for the United States Atomic Energy Commission.—AP and UPI.

FIGURE 32   This article, published on the front page of *The Times*, reflects the excitement caused by the discovery of the J/ψ but it contains several errors. One concerns the date of the discovery—it was announced on 11 November, not on 16 November as the text implies. How many errors of physics can you spot?

FIGURE 30   Burton Richter (centre) led the team of physicists from SLAC and the Lawrence Berkeley laboratory that discovered the J/ψ at SLAC. This photograph was taken on 10 November 1974 soon after the discovery of the J/ψ.

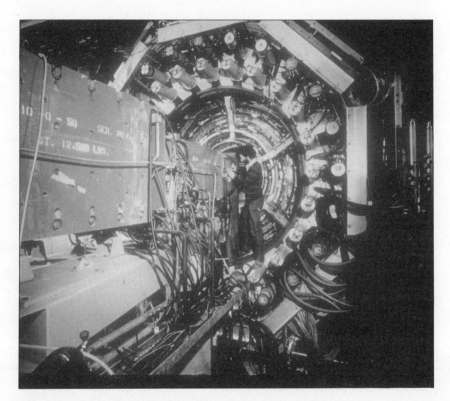

FIGURE 31   The J/ψ was discovered at SLAC using this detector.

The most popular theory of the J/ψ was based on quantum chromodynamics and on the idea that the meson contained a c (charm) quark and a $\bar{c}$ antiquark:

$$
\begin{array}{llll}
 & J/\psi & c & \bar{c} \\
Q & 0 & = \tfrac{2}{3} & -\tfrac{2}{3} \\
B & 0 & = \tfrac{1}{3} & -\tfrac{1}{3} \\
S & 0 & = 0 & +0 \\
C & 0 & = 1 & -1 \\
\end{array}
$$

Hence, according to the $c\bar{c}$ theory of the J/ψ, the particle has hidden charm—the charm of its c quark cancels that of its $\bar{c}$ antiquark, giving the J/ψ zero net charm. Also, the $c\bar{c}$ theory said that the rest mass of the parti-

NAKED CHARM

cle is very high compared with that of ordinary hadrons because the rest mass of the c quark is considerably greater than the rest masses of the u, d and s quarks (and their antiparticles), the constituents of ordinary hadrons*.

According to the c$\bar{\text{c}}$ theory, the ψ' is simply the first excited state of the c$\bar{\text{c}}$ pair, whose lowest energy state corresponds to the J/ψ. It was also predicted using the theory that there should be other c$\bar{\text{c}}$ mesons with even higher rest masses, corresponding to higher-energy states. These predictions were soon verified experimentally and the c$\bar{\text{c}}$ theory rapidly gained ascendancy over its rivals. Indeed, the c$\bar{\text{c}}$ theory was widely believed to be correct by the spring of 1975, and it is now universally accepted.

Any lingering doubts about the validity of the c$\bar{\text{c}}$ theory were dispelled in 1975 and 1976 by the discoveries of the other hadrons that contained c quarks (or $\bar{\text{c}}$ antiquarks) in combination with the familiar u, d and s quarks (and their antiparticles). For example, the $D^+ = c\bar{d}$ and $D^0 = c\bar{u}$ mesons were discovered in an e^+e^- colliding beam experiment at SLAC in the summer of 1976. These mesons had precisely the properties predicted by the quark model, notably non-zero charm, or **naked charm** as it is usually called:

$$D^+ = c \quad \bar{d}$$
$$Q \quad 1 \quad = \tfrac{2}{3} + \tfrac{1}{3}$$
$$B \quad 0 \quad = \tfrac{1}{3} - \tfrac{1}{3}$$
$$S \quad 0 \quad = 0 + 0$$
$$C \quad 1 \quad = 1 + 0$$

$$D^0 = c \quad \bar{u}$$
$$Q \quad 0 \quad = \tfrac{2}{3} - \tfrac{2}{3}$$
$$B \quad 0 \quad = \tfrac{1}{3} - \tfrac{1}{3}$$
$$S \quad 0 \quad = 0 + 0$$
$$C \quad 1 \quad = 1 + 0$$

Experiments also showed that charm was, like strangeness, conserved in strong and electromagnetic interactions but not in weak interactions, just as Glashow, Iliopoulos and Maiani had predicted.

In 1976, Samuel Ting (Figure 29) and Burton Richter (Figure 30), the leaders of the teams that discovered the J/ψ particle, were awarded the Nobel Prize in physics for 'their pioneering work in the discovery of a heavy [hadron] of a new kind'. As you have seen, it was this monumental discovery that sparked off the excitement and confusion of the November Revolution—only later did it become clear that the junta were the proponents of charm.

6.2 THE DISCOVERY OF A NEW LEPTON AND THE CONSEQUENCES

No sooner had the four-quark, four-lepton symmetry been completed by the discovery of the charm quark, than there were rumours from SLAC that a group of experimenters there had found evidence in e^+e^- colliding-beam experiments for a new, charged lepton with exceptionally high rest mass (around $1.8\,\text{GeV}/c^2$). The existence of such a lepton was certainly not expected and, if its discovery were confirmed, the recently realized quark–lepton symmetry would be destroyed. Small wonder, then, that one notable physicist remarked in a seminar that he hoped the new lepton would 'go away'.

The team of experimenters at SLAC, led by Martin Perl, found after months of pains-taking analysis that their data on e^+e^- collisions could be understood only if they were observing a new charged heavy lepton, which they called the τ^- (pronounced tau minus), produced with its antiparticle, the τ^+.

$$e^+ + e^- \rightarrow \tau^+ + \tau^-$$

* The exceptionally long lifetime of the J/ψ was also explained by the c$\bar{\text{c}}$ theory, which predicts that the particle's strong decays are suppressed to a level comparable with electromagnetic decays.

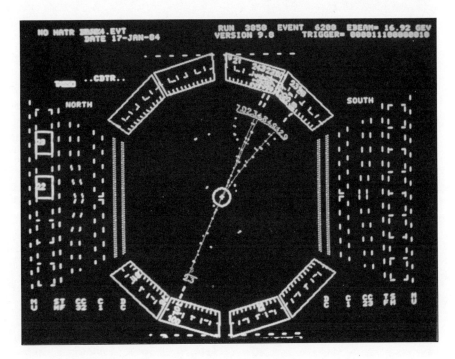

FIGURE 33 The tracks of the charged particles produced when a τ^+ and a τ^- are produced when an electron and a positron collide. (The collision takes place at the centre of the detector.) The τ^+ decays into a μ^+ (which travels towards the bottom left) and, we believe, into a $\bar{\nu}_\tau$ and a ν_μ (both of which have no charge and therefore do not leave a tell-tale track). The τ^- decays into two π^- particles, a π^+ and, we believe, into a ν_τ, which leaves no track.

For several months, particle physicists were far from certain that the SLAC team really had observed this reaction. One of the main reasons for this scepticism was that the discovery was not confirmed by analyses of e^+e^- collisions at the DESY (pronounced daisy) laboratory in West Germany. However, the DESY group did eventually confirm the discovery in 1975 (Figure 33).

The rest masses of the τ^- and τ^+ have now been pinned down to approximately $1.78 \, \text{GeV}/c^2$—roughly 17 times the rest mass of the next heaviest lepton, the μ^-, and roughly 3 500 times the rest mass of the electron!

☐ Does the existence of the τ^- suggest that there exist any more leptons?

■ Yes. It is reasonable to expect that the τ^- should have an associated neutrino ν_τ, with zero charge and zero (or nearly zero) rest mass, just as the electron e^- and mu minus μ^- have associated neutrinos, ν_e and ν_μ respectively, with precisely analogous properties.

☐ What type of interactions do you expect the tau neutrino ν_τ to have?

■ Assuming that the ν_τ has properties that are similar to the other neutrinos (ν_e and ν_μ), you should expect that it has only gravitational and weak interactions. If the particle has zero charge it will not interact electromagnetically. Also, because it is a lepton, it cannot have strong interactions.

By the same reasoning, you should expect the antilepton τ^+ to have an associated antineutrino $\bar{\nu}_\tau$ which has zero charge and zero (or nearly zero) rest mass, and which interacts only gravitationally and weakly.

At the time of writing, neither the ν_τ nor the $\bar{\nu}_\tau$ has been discovered, but that is not at all worrying, as such fundamental particles with only weak and gravitational interactions will be extremely hard to detect. It is, however, expected that experiments will confirm the existence of the ν_τ and $\bar{\nu}_\tau$ during the lifetime of the Course. We shall keep you keep informed in the errata sheets!

TOPNESS

BOTTOMNESS

NAKED BOTTOM

As you will have realized, the τ^- and ν_τ ruined the lepton–quark symmetry:

$$\begin{pmatrix} e^- & \mu^- & \tau^- \\ \nu_e & \nu_\mu & \nu_\tau \end{pmatrix} \quad \begin{pmatrix} u & c & \\ d & s & \end{pmatrix}$$

☐ Can you now predict the existence of two more fundamental particles?

■ It should be plain that the lepton–quark symmetry can be restored (in theory at least) by postulating the existence of two more quarks. This was precisely what was done—the new quarks were called top and bottom (or sometimes truth and beauty). *Enter the symbols* t *and* b *in the gaps above, putting the* t *next to the charm quark* c, *and the* b *next to the strange quark* s.

What could be predicted about the properties of the newly proposed quarks?

ITQ 6 (a) What do you predict to be the charge and baryon number of the t and b quarks? Enter your answers in Table 10.

(b) Is it possible to predict the rest masses of the t and b quarks?

TABLE 10   Properties of six quarks

Type of quark	Charge Q	Baryon number B	Strangeness S	Charm C	Bottomness B	Topness T
u	$+\frac{2}{3}$	$\frac{1}{3}$	0	0	0	0
d	$-\frac{1}{3}$	$\frac{1}{3}$	0	0	0	0
c	$+\frac{2}{3}$	$\frac{1}{3}$	0	1	0	0
s	$-\frac{1}{3}$	$\frac{1}{3}$	-1	0	0	0
t			0	0	0	1
b			0	0	-1	0

In Table 10, you can see that the t and b quarks were both predicted to have zero strangeness and charm and that they should each have a characteristic property. The t and b quarks are predicted respectively to have the intrinsic properties of **topness** and **bottomness**. These properties were expected to be analogous to strangeness and charm, in the sense that they should be conserved in strong and electromagnetic interactions, but not in weak interactions.

ITQ 7 (a) What are the predicted charge, baryon number, strangeness, charm, bottomness and topness of the $\bar{t}$ and $\bar{b}$ antiquarks?

(b) What are the predicted rest masses of the $\bar{t}$ and $\bar{b}$ antiquarks in terms of the corresponding rest masses of the t and b quarks?

It is one thing to predict the existence of new quarks, but it is quite another to detect them. Would hadrons that contained t and b quarks (and their antiparticles) be detected?

In the summer of 1977, a group of experimenters at Fermilab (near Chicago) led by the American physicist Leon Lederman, observed a new hadron Υ (pronounced upsilon) which has the extraordinarily high rest mass of approximately $9.5\,\text{GeV}/c^2$, and a remarkably long lifetime compared with ordinary hadrons (ones that have a rest mass of about $1\,\text{GeV}/c^2$: see Figure 19). The properties of the Υ could be understood if it contained a b quark and a $\bar{b}$ antiquark ($\Upsilon = b\bar{b}$). Within two months, the group had detected more hadrons (Υ', Υ'' and Υ''') with even higher rest masses, and these particles were interpreted as excited states of the $b\bar{b}$ pair. This $b\bar{b}$ theory of the new hadrons was soon generally accepted by the high-energy physics community—the b quark (and its antiparticle) had been 'identified', and its rest mass was approximately $5\,\text{GeV}/c^2$.

The discovery of the Υ was not nearly as dramatic as that of the J/ψ. Drama depends considerably on the element of surprise, and whereas in 1974 very few physicists were expecting the $c\bar{c}$ mesons to be discovered, in 1977 many were actually *awaiting* the arrival of the $b\bar{b}$ family! You will not

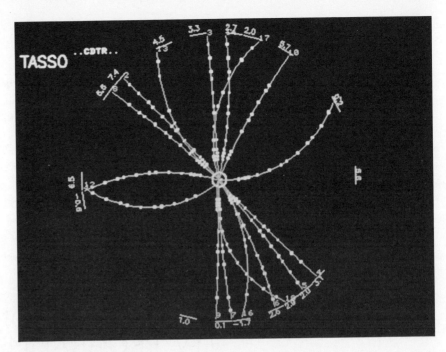

FIGURE 34 The decay of a naked bottom. Note that only the tracks of *charged* particles are observed.

be surprised to learn that hadrons with non-zero bottomness were subsequently observed (Figure 34) with the predicted properties. The observation of these particles, which are sometimes called **naked bottoms**, removed any doubts about the validity of the $b\bar{b}$ theory of the Υ. The analogy with the case of charm is complete.

What about the t quark? At the time of going to print (spring 1988), there is no clear evidence for the existence of hadrons that contain it (or its antiparticle). However, very few physicists doubt that these hadrons will eventually be discovered, such is the confidence in the lepton–quark symmetry.

You may well be wondering if there exist any more leptons and quarks. This is a perfectly valid point. Perhaps the current six lepton–six quark symmetry will one day be ruined by the discovery of an extra lepton or quark?

SUMMARY OF SECTION 6

1 It is essential theoretically that there is a lepton–quark symmetry, according to which the number of pairs of leptons (one with charge -1, the other with charge 0) is equal to the number of pairs of quarks (one with charge $+\frac{2}{3}$, the other with charge $-\frac{1}{3}$).

2 If the lepton–quark symmetry is incomplete, it must be restored by postulating the existence of the missing particle(s). In this way, the symmetry can be used to predict the existence of fundamental particles (leptons and quarks).

3 The identification of the charm quark and its antiparticle as the constituents of the J/ψ particle ($= c\bar{c}$), enabled the four lepton–four quark symmetry to be completed

$$Q = -1 \quad \rightarrow \quad \begin{pmatrix} e^- & \mu^- \\ \nu_e & \nu_\mu \end{pmatrix} \quad \begin{pmatrix} u & c \\ d & s \end{pmatrix} \quad \leftarrow \quad Q = +\frac{2}{3} \\ Q = 0 \quad \rightarrow \quad \qquad\qquad\qquad\qquad\qquad \leftarrow \quad Q = -\frac{1}{3}$$

4 The unexpected discovery of the τ^- lepton led to the prediction of the ν_τ and also, in order to complete the six lepton–six quark symmetry, to the prediction of two more quarks. These new quarks were called top (t) and bottom (b):

GAUGE BOSONS

PHOTON

INTERMEDIATE VECTOR
BOSONS

$$Q = -1 \rightarrow \begin{pmatrix} e^- & \mu^- & \tau^- \\ \nu_e & \nu_\mu & \nu_\tau \end{pmatrix} \quad \begin{pmatrix} u & c & t \\ d & s & b \end{pmatrix} \leftarrow Q = +\tfrac{2}{3} \\ Q = 0 \rightarrow \qquad\qquad\qquad\qquad\qquad\qquad\quad \leftarrow Q = -\tfrac{1}{3}$$

SAQ 12 Which one of the following entities (a)–(e) is currently believed to have constituents?

(a) J/ψ; (b) τ^-; (c) $\bar{\nu}_\tau$; (d) t; (e) $\bar{b}$.

SAQ 13 What are the charge, baryon number, strangeness, charm, topness and bottomness of the following combinations of quarks and anti-quarks?

(a) c$\bar{s}$; (b) t$\bar{u}$.

7 GAUGE BOSONS (TV PROGRAMME)

In this Section, we shall consider the class of fundamental particles known as gauge bosons (pronounced boze-ons). There are four varieties of these particles, each of which is associated with one of the types of fundamental *interaction*. After considering the nature of gauge bosons in general, the four varieties will be considered in turn.

7.1 GAUGE BOSONS—MEDIATORS OF FUNDAMENTAL INTERACTIONS

You have already seen that fundamental particles can interact in four ways—strongly, electromagnetically, weakly and gravitationally. But what is the *mechanism* that underlies these interactions? It is possible to derive some insight into that question using a simple picture based on the idea of *particle exchange*.

An interaction between two fundamental particles can be understood simply in terms of the exchange of another fundamental particle, a **gauge boson** (Figure 35). The interaction is said to be *mediated* by the gauge boson. In order to see how such a mechanism is plausible, picture two ice-skaters on an ice-rink (Figure 36). If skater A throws a ball to skater B, they are propelled *away from* each other, whereas if A throws a boomerang to B, they are propelled *towards* each other. Hence, the skaters' interactions—repulsive or attractive—are 'mediated' by the objects that they exchange. These large-scale situations should give you some intuitive understanding of how fundamental interactions between fundamental particles can be mediated by the exchange of another particle. However, you should not take the 'exchange picture' literally, because it is only an analogy. A complete and rigorous understanding of the role of gauge bosons can be obtained only by using the theories of quantum mechanics and special relativity.

FIGURE 35   Each fundamental interaction between fundamental particles is mediated by a characteristic type of gauge boson.

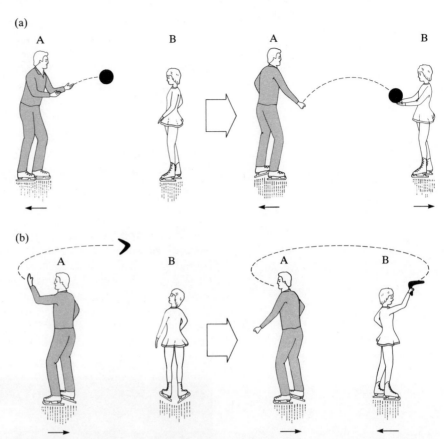

FIGURE 36 Interactions that can occur between two ice-skaters when they exchange (a) a heavy object, (b) a boomerang.

Each type of fundamental interaction is mediated by a characteristic type of gauge boson (Figure 37): electromagnetic interactions are mediated by the photon, weak interactions by intermediate vector bosons, strong interactions by gluons and gravitational interactions by the graviton. Each of these gauge bosons has a characteristic rest mass and electrical charge (and each one has zero values of baryon number, strangeness, charm, topness and bottomness).

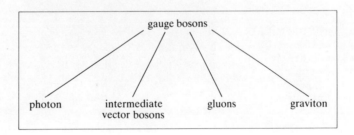

FIGURE 37 The four types of gauge boson.

7.2 TYPES OF GAUGE BOSON

7.2.1 THE PHOTON

The **photon**, normally denoted by the symbol γ, is the fundamental particle that mediates electromagnetic interactions. It is electrically neutral and has zero rest mass.

The photon is its own antiparticle; in other words, the antiparticle of a photon is a photon. Such a fundamental particle is said to be self-conjugate (all neutral gauge bosons are of this type).

7.2.2 INTERMEDIATE VECTOR BOSONS

In the late 1950s, it was suggested that weak interactions are mediated by **intermediate vector bosons**, W^+, W^- and Z, although no theory could describe the properties of the hypothetical particles and there was no evidence whatever for their existence. However, in 1967 there was put forward

WEINBERG–SALAM
THEORY

GLUON

a remarkable theory that could describe the behaviour of these gauge bosons and that could predict their masses in terms of other experimentally observable quantities. This theory was formulated independently by the American physicist Steven Weinberg and the Pakistani physicist Abdus Salam, each of whom used ideas that had been developed by others, notably Glashow. The **Weinberg-Salam theory** described both weak and electromagnetic interactions within a single theory—it gave a *unified* description of two fundamental interactions*.

The first indirect evidence that firmly supported the predictions of the Weinberg–Salam theory concerned weak interactions such as

$$\nu_\mu + p \rightarrow \nu_\mu + p$$
$$\nu_\mu + e^- \rightarrow \nu_\mu + e^-$$

The Weinberg–Salam theory predicted that these reactions should occur, whereas previous theories of the weak interaction predicted that they should *not* be observed. Hence, when these reactions were observed at CERN in 1973, it was hailed as a triumph for the theory. Weinberg, Salam and Glashow (Figure 38) were subsequently awarded the 1979 Nobel Prize in physics for their work, even though the W^+, W^- and Z—on whose existence the credibility of the theory depended—had not actually been observed!

FIGURE 38   Sheldon Glashow (left), Abdus Salam (centre) and Steven Weinberg (right) were awarded the 1979 Nobel Prize in physics 'for their contributions to the theory of the unified weak and electromagnetic interaction'.

Weinberg and Salam's theory predicted that the rest masses of the intermediate vector bosons are extraordinarily high. It was expected that the rest mass of the W^+ and its antiparticle the W^- should be approximately $80\,\text{GeV}/c^2$, and that the rest mass of the Z should be approximately $90\,\text{GeV}/c^2$. Alas, these predictions could not be checked because the energies available at the particle accelerators at the time were far too low for particles of such high rest masses to be produced.

Most physicists were of the opinion that it would be decades before accelerators of sufficiently high energy would be available to check the predictions. However, Carlo Rubbia, a leading Italian experimenter, believed otherwise. In 1976, he and some collaborators suggested that if the intermediate vector bosons existed and if they had roughly the properties suggested by the Weinberg–Salam theory, then it should just be possible to detect them using CERN's SPS (Super Proton Synchrotron) accelerator (Figure 8). This machine was originally designed to generate 500 GeV protons for fixed-

* Although the weak and electromagnetic interactions are generally regarded as having been unified by the Weinberg–Salam theory, we shall continue to refer to the two types of interactions as being separate, in order to be consistent with the material earlier in the text.

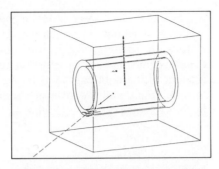

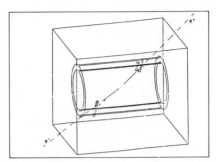

FIGURE 39 As described in the TV programme 'The Search for the W and Z', the existence of W particles was confirmed by the observation of the tell-tale straight tracks of electrons and muons. The track in this record is left by a muon after the decay $W^- \rightarrow \mu^- + \bar{v}_\mu$. (The antineutrino does not leave a track because it has no charge.)

FIGURE 40 As described in the TV programme, the existence of the Z was confirmed by the observation of tell-tale tracks left by e^+e^- (and $\mu^+\mu^-$) decay products of the particle. In this record, the tracks are left by an electron and a positron, $Z \rightarrow e^+ + e^-$. This record, and the one in Figure 39, were obtained using drift chambers.

FIGURE 41 Carlo Rubbia (left) and Simon van der Meer (right) were awarded the 1984 Nobel Prize for physics for 'the discovery of the [gauge bosons] W and Z, communicators of the weak interaction'.

target experiments, but the energy of these protons was too low to enable intermediate vector bosons to be produced. However, Rubbia and his collaborators proposed that the SPS could be converted into a machine that could be used to do colliding-beam experiments with 270 GeV protons and 270 GeV antiprotons. The conversion was made possible by advances in accelerator technology made by the Dutch physicist Simon van der Meer.

Calculations showed that, if the Weinberg–Salam theory were correct, it should be possible to observe certain types of decay of the intermediate vector bosons, notably

$$W^+ \rightarrow \mu^+ + v_\mu$$
$$W^- \rightarrow \mu^- + \bar{v}_\mu$$
$$Z \rightarrow e^+ + e^-$$

After the proposal had been carefully evaluated, CERN decided to go ahead with the project, even though many physicists firmly believed that the outcome would be an expensive fiasco, with no clear evidence for intermediate vector bosons and an acutely embarrassing loss of kudos for European science. The prestige of CERN was at stake.

The search for the intermediate vector bosons was carried out by two teams, one of which was led by Rubbia, with his characteristic flair and exuberance. In the TV programme 'The search for the W and Z', we follow the progress of Rubbia's team of 135 physicists, from the beginnings of the project to the tentative announcement of the discoveries of the W^+ and W^- in January 1983. The group found that, just as Weinberg and Salam's theory had predicted, the rest masses of the W particles were around $80 \, \text{GeV}/c^2$ and that they could decay into a charged lepton and a neutrino (Figure 39). The group later confirmed the existence of the Z (Figure 40), which had precisely the properties expected on the basis of the Weinberg–Salam theory. Few scientists were surprised when the 1984 Nobel Prize for physics was awarded jointly to Carlo Rubbia and Simon van der Meer (Figure 41).

7.2.3 GLUONS

The strong interactions between quarks (and antiquarks) are mediated by gauge bosons that Gell-Mann called **gluons**. According to quantum chromodynamics, there are eight different gluons $g_1, g_2, \ldots, g_8$, each of which has 'colour' but zero rest mass and zero electrical charge. Isolated gluons have never been detected and, according to QCD theory, they never

GRAVITON

proton

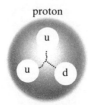

neutron

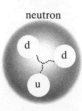

FIGURE 42 In the proton and the neutron, the constituent quarks are bound together by gluons (shown here as wavy dotted lines).

will be! However, there is much indirect but compelling evidence for the existence of gluons. For example, data from experiments in which charged leptons are scattered by protons and neutrons can be understood only if these hadrons have other constituents besides u and d quarks. An excellent account of the data can be given by quantum chromodynamics, according to which the u and d quarks are bound together in a proton and a neutron by the exchange of gluons (Figure 42).

7.2.4 THE GRAVITON

It is believed on theoretical grounds that gravitational interactions are mediated by a gauge boson known as the **graviton**, G. This particle has not yet been observed, but it is predicted to have zero rest mass and zero charge. Experimenters do not expect to be able to detect gravitons in the foreseeable future—they are even more difficult to detect than the intermediate vector bosons! The graviton awaits its Rubbia.

SUMMARY OF SECTION 7

1 Gauge bosons are fundamental particles that mediate fundamental interactions.

2 A characteristic type of gauge boson is associated with each type of fundamental interaction. Electromagnetic interactions are mediated by the photon, weak interactions by intermediate vector bosons, strong interactions by gluons. Gravitational interactions are believed to be mediated by the graviton, although this gauge boson has not yet been detected.

SAQ 14 Which one of the following statements about gauge bosons is correct? Explain your answer.

(a) The photon is not a fundamental particle.

(b) Because the decay $W^+ \rightarrow \mu^+ + \nu_\mu$ has been observed, it can be concluded correctly that the W^+ contains a μ^+ and a ν_μ.

(c) Each proton and neutron in an atomic nucleus contains quarks bound together by gluons.

8 PARTICLE PHYSICS IN PERSPECTIVE

In this Unit, you have seen that it is currently believed that there are three types of fundamental particle—leptons, quarks and gauge bosons. You have also seen that there are four types of fundamental interaction—gravitational, strong, weak and electromagnetic (although the latter two have been described in a unified way by the Weinberg–Salam theory). The fundamental particles are listed in Table 11 with their charges and rest masses.

Through the eyes of a particle physicist, a seemingly uncomplicated scene on Earth has extraordinary richness and complexity. For example, consider, from the particle physicist's point of view, the scene that you met at the beginning of the Unit (Figure 43).

Cosmic rays, which consist ultimately of certain quarks, leptons and gauge bosons, are raining down on the whole scene, and antineutrinos are emerging from the ground (owing to radioactive decay processes within the Earth). All the matter is attracted towards the Earth by gravitational interactions, which are mediated by gravitons. The atomic constituents of the matter in turn consist of electrons and nuclei; the electrons are examples of leptons and the nuclei consist of combinations of u and d quarks. The elec-

TABLE 11 The fundamental particles*

Particle	Symbol	Charge	Rest mass /(GeV/c^2)
LEPTONS			
electron	e^-	-1	5.11×10^{-4}
mu minus	μ^-	-1	1.06×10^{-1}
tau minus	τ^-	-1	1.78
electron neutrino	ν_e	0	≈ 0
muon neutrino	ν_μ	0	≈ 0
tau neutrino	ν_τ?	0	≈ 0
QUARKS			
up	u	$\frac{2}{3}$	≈ 0.005
down	d	$-\frac{1}{3}$	≈ 0.01
charm	c	$\frac{2}{3}$	≈ 1.3
strange	s	$-\frac{1}{3}$	≈ 0.2
top	t?	$\frac{2}{3}$	
bottom	b	$-\frac{1}{3}$	≈ 5
GAUGE BOSONS			
photon	γ	0	0
intermediate vector bosons	$\begin{cases} W^+ \\ W^- \\ Z \end{cases}$	$\begin{matrix} 1 \\ -1 \\ 0 \end{matrix}$	$\begin{matrix} 82 \\ 82 \\ 93 \end{matrix}$
gluons	$g_1, \ldots, g_8$	0	0
graviton	G?	0	0

* Note that there also exist antileptons and antiquarks (Sections 3 and 5).

FIGURE 43 A 'fundamental' view of the scene shown in Figure 1.

BIG BANG

trons in an atom are bound to the atom's nucleus by the electromagnetic interaction, and the quarks in the nucleus are held together by the fundamental strong interaction, mediated by gluons. From the Sun, there is raining down both photons (gauge bosons) and neutrinos (leptons).

The formulation of such a qualitative description is not normally the province of particle physicists, who deal mainly in terms of rigorously defined theories of fundamental particles and their interactions. In this Unit, the details of such theories (e.g. quantum chromodynamics and the Weinberg–Salam theory) have been avoided and we have concentrated on the *results* of the theories and on their relevance to the search for fundamental particles. As you have probably gathered, the search is by no means at an end, and many profound questions remain to be answered. For example:

1 *Do there exist more quarks, leptons and gauge bosons?* It is, of course, quite possible that experimenters will detect more of these particles.

2 *Are leptons, quarks and gauge bosons really fundamental?* Perhaps experimenters will show that these types of particle actually have constituents after all?

3 *Is it possible to formulate a single, unified theory that describes all the possible fundamental interactions between all of the fundamental particles?* This is currently one of the central questions of theoretical particle physics. In one line of research that has proved particularly fruitful, it is suggested that the fundamental entities of matter are 'string-like' (i.e. *not* point-like), on a scale of 10^{-35} m. This idea will be hard to test because present experiments probe the structure of matter down to the comparatively huge scale of 10^{-18} m!

One of the most exciting topics in contemporary science concerns the application of the fundamental laws of physics to the evolution of the Universe. Using these laws in conjunction with a wealth of astronomical data, it has been established (to the satisfaction of most scientists) that the Universe began in an event known as the **Big Bang**. In this event, which is believed to have occurred approximately 16 000 million years ago, space, time, matter and energy were actually created. At first, the Universe was extremely hot and dense but subsequently it expanded and cooled.

Some of the highlights in the evolution of the Universe (according to current theories) are shown in Figure 44. As you can see from this Figure, approximately 10^{-35} seconds after the Big Bang the Universe contained leptons, quarks and gauge bosons (and their antiparticles), moving around with extremely high energy. Within about a thousandth of a second, the quarks and antiquarks cooled sufficiently to form hadrons. After about a minute, the energies of protons and neutrons were sufficiently low that they could 'stick together' to form atomic nuclei, but it was not until about 10 000 years later that the energies of electrons and nuclei were low enough for stable chemical elements to be formed. On the cosmic timescale of Figure 44, terrestrial rocks were formed quite recently and life on Earth began 'yesterday', so to speak!

The evolution of the Universe certainly cannot be said to be fully understood, because there are many stages of the process that remain unclear. There is some doubt about the details of the processes going on at times less than 10^{-12} s after the Big Bang, and even physicists do not dare to say with confidence what was going on much before 10^{-35} s after the beginning of the Universe! However, it is fair to say that scientists are now confident that they have at least a basic understanding of how the Universe has evolved from the beginning of time to the present day. This understanding has been achieved by an interdisciplinary collaboration—biologists, chemists and Earth scientists have been involved, as well as physicists.

The attempts made to understand the evolution of the Universe have been made possible by an interplay of scientific theory and experiment. It is remarkable that scientists on Earth, a mere speck in the cosmos, have made so much progress in understanding 16 000 million years or so of the Universe's history, using ideas that have been developed (for the most part)

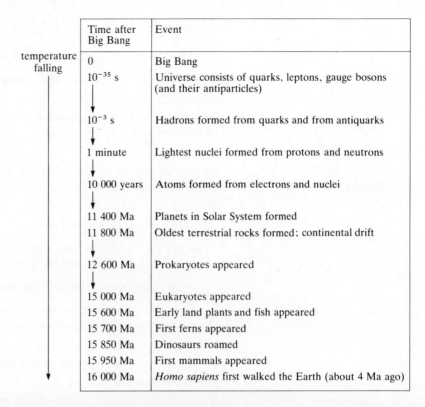

temperature falling

Time after Big Bang	Event
0	Big Bang
10^{-35} s	Universe consists of quarks, leptons, gauge bosons (and their antiparticles)
10^{-3} s	Hadrons formed from quarks and from antiquarks
1 minute	Lightest nuclei formed from protons and neutrons
10 000 years	Atoms formed from electrons and nuclei
11 400 Ma	Planets in Solar System formed
11 800 Ma	Oldest terrestrial rocks formed; continental drift
12 600 Ma	Prokaryotes appeared
15 000 Ma	Eukaryotes appeared
15 600 Ma	Early land plants and fish appeared
15 700 Ma	First ferns appeared
15 850 Ma	Dinosaurs roamed
15 950 Ma	First mammals appeared
16 000 Ma	*Homo sapiens* first walked the Earth (about 4 Ma ago)

FIGURE 44 Some notable events since the Big Bang. In this Figure, it is assumed in the nine lowest entries that *Homo sapiens* first walked the Earth 16 000 million years after the Big Bang. However, this figure has actually been determined only to within an uncertainty of several thousand million years, so the preceding eight entries have the same uncertainty!

only in the last 100 years. This progress is surely one of the greatest scientific achievements of the 20th century. As Steven Weinberg has reflected in his book about the origin of the Universe:

> Men and women are not content to comfort themselves with tales of gods and giants, or to confine their thoughts to the daily affairs of life; they also build telescopes and satellites and accelerators, and sit at their desks for endless hours working out the meaning of the data they gather. The effort to understand the universe is one of the very few things that lifts human life a little above the level of farce, and gives it some of the grace of tragedy.
>
> (Epilogue to *The First Three Minutes*)

FURTHER READING

Particles and Fields (1980), W. H. Freeman and Company. This is a collection of key articles on particle physics that have been published between 1953 and 1979 in *Scientific American*, an excellent source of articles on new developments in the subject. The article by Glashow on quantum chromodynamics is particularly strongly recommended.

Close, F., Marten, M. and Sutton, C. (1987) *The Particle Explosion*, Oxford University Press. A beautifully illustrated and easy-to-read survey of the world of particle physics.

Parker, B. (1987) *Search for a Supertheory: From Atoms to Superstrings*, Plenum. A fairly advanced text that gives a clear account of the developments that have led to the formulation of 'string' theories.

Sutton, C. (ed.) (1985) *Building the Universe*, Blackwell and New Scientist. This is a selection of *New Scientist* articles on particle physics, linked by helpful explanatory passages by the editor.

Watkins, P. (1986) *The Story of the W and Z*, Cambridge University Press. A readable account of the discovery of the intermediate vector bosons, with much useful background material, written at an elementary level.

Weinberg, S. (1977) *The First Three Minutes*, André Deutsch. A popular account of the physics of the Big Bang, written by one of the outstanding theoreticians of recent times.

OBJECTIVES FOR UNIT 32

After you have worked through this Unit, you should be able to:

1 Explain the meaning of, and use correctly, all the terms flagged in the text.

2 Recall that leptons, quarks and gauge bosons are currently believed to be fundamental particles. (*SAQs 1, 5, 9, 10, 12 and 14*)

3 State the rest mass, charge, baryon number etc. of an antiparticle, given the corresponding properties of the corresponding particle. (*ITQs 1, 5 and 7, SAQ 5*)

4 Convert from units of kilograms to units of GeV/c^2 and from units of joules to units of GeV. (*SAQs 3 and 4*)

5 Apply the basic principles that underlie the operation of particle accelerators and detectors. (*SAQs 2–4*)

6 Recall the properties and interactions of leptons. (*ITQ 2, SAQs 5, 6 and 9*)

7 Apply the conservation laws of charge, baryon number, strangeness, charm, topness and bottomness to examples of strong interactions. (*ITQs 3 and 4, SAQs 7 and 8*)

8 Recall the four types of interaction that are currently believed to be fundamental. (*SAQ 10*)

9 Apply the simple quark model. (*SAQs 11 and 13*)

10 State the consequences of a breakdown of the lepton–quark symmetry. (*ITQs 6 and 7*)

11 Describe the role played by gauge bosons in mediating fundamental interactions. (*SAQ 14*)

ITQ ANSWERS AND COMMENTS

ITQ 1 The positron e^+ has charge $+1$ (in units of the proton's charge e) and rest mass $5.11 \times 10^{-4} \, GeV/c^2$, the mu plus μ^+ has charge $+1$ and rest mass $1.06 \times 10^{-1} \, GeV/c^2$; both antineutrinos $\bar{\nu}_e$ and $\bar{\nu}_\mu$ have zero charge and zero (or nearly zero) rest mass. The properties follow from the definition of antiparticle: an antiparticle has the *opposite* charge but the *same* rest mass as the corresponding particle.

ITQ 2 The charged leptons and antileptons (e^-, e^+, μ^- and μ^+) can interact electromagnetically because they have charge, and they can interact gravitationally, in common with all other particles and antiparticles. By the same token, neutrinos and antineutrinos can also interact gravitationally.

ITQ 3 Reaction (c) is forbidden:

(c)
$$p + p \not\rightarrow p + p + \pi^+ + \pi^- + \pi^+$$
$$Q \quad +1 \quad +1 \quad +1 \quad +1 \quad +1 \quad -1 \quad +1$$
$$+2 \neq +3 \qquad Q \text{ not conserved}$$

Reactions (a) and (b) are allowed, according to charge conservation:

(a)
$$p + p \rightarrow p + p$$
$$Q \quad +1 \quad +1 \quad +1 \quad +1$$
$$+2 = +2 \qquad Q \text{ conserved}$$

(b)
$$p + p \rightarrow p + p + \pi^+ + \pi^-$$
$$Q \quad +1 \quad +1 \quad +1 \quad +1 \quad +1 \quad -1$$
$$+2 = +2 \qquad Q \text{ conserved}$$

ITQ 4 Reaction (b) is forbidden because baryon number is not conserved:

(b)
$$p + p \not\rightarrow \pi^+ + p + n + n$$
$$B \quad 1 \quad 1 \quad 0 \quad 1 \quad 1 \quad 1$$
$$2 \neq 3 \qquad B \text{ not conserved}$$

In reactions (a) and (c), baryon number and charge are both conserved, so neither reaction is forbidden:

(a)
$$p + p \rightarrow \pi^+ + p + n$$
$$Q \quad 1 \quad 1 \quad 1 \quad 1 \quad 0$$
$$2 = 2 \qquad Q \text{ conserved}$$
$$B \quad 1 \quad 1 \quad 0 \quad 1 \quad 1$$
$$2 = 2 \qquad B \text{ conserved}$$

(c)
$$p + p \rightarrow p + p + \pi^0 + \pi^0$$
$$Q \quad 1 \quad 1 \quad 1 \quad 1 \quad 0 \quad 0$$
$$2 = 2 \qquad Q \text{ conserved}$$
$$B \quad 1 \quad 1 \quad 1 \quad 1 \quad 0 \quad 0$$
$$2 = 2 \qquad B \text{ conserved}$$

ITQ 5 The $\bar{c}$ antiquark should have charge $-\frac{2}{3}$, baryon number $-\frac{1}{3}$, strangeness 0, charm -1 and a rest mass of approximately $1.5\,\text{GeV}/c^2$. These properties follow from the definition of an antiparticle: an antiparticle has the *opposite* charge, baryon number, strangeness and charm, but the *same* rest mass as the corresponding particle.

ITQ 6 (a) The t and b quarks should, in common with the other quarks, have baryon number $\frac{1}{3}$. The t quark should, in common with the u and c quarks, have charge $+\frac{2}{3}$, whereas the b quark should, in common with the d and s quarks, have charge $-\frac{1}{3}$.

(b) No, you should not be able to predict the rest masses of the t and b quarks. We certainly have not shown in the text how such predictions could be made!

ITQ 7 (a) For the $\bar{t}$ antiquark: $Q = -\frac{2}{3}$, $B = -\frac{1}{3}$, $C = 0$, $B = 0$, $T = -1$. For the $\bar{b}$ antiquark $Q = +\frac{1}{3}$, $B = -\frac{1}{3}$, $C = 0$, $B = 1$, $T = 0$. These values are opposite to those of the corresponding quarks.

(b) The rest mass of the $\bar{t}$ should be the same as that of the t, and the rest mass of the $\bar{b}$ should be the same as that of the b. Remember, the rest mass of an antiparticle is the same as that of the corresponding particle.

SAQ ANSWERS AND COMMENTS

SAQ 1 None, because each of the entities has constituents. A chlorine molecule consists of chlorine atoms; a helium atom consists of a helium nucleus and two electrons; a uranium nucleus consists of protons and neutrons.

SAQ 2 Other particles can be produced 'out of thin air' when two particles collide because some of the total kinetic energy of the original particles can be converted into the energy of the rest masses of the produced particles. Energy is, as always, conserved:

energy equiv. to total rest mass of particles before the collision	+ kinetic energy of particles before the collision	= energy equiv. to total rest mass of particles after the collision	+ kinetic energy of particles after the collision

SAQ 3 (a) No, because the π^0 has no charge. Only charged particles can leave a track in a drift chamber.

(b) No. According to the special theory of relativity, the speed of a particle can never exceed the speed of light in a vacuum, $c \approx 3 \times 10^8\,\text{m s}^{-1}$.

(c) $0.14\,\text{GeV}/c^2$.

On the back cover of these Units, it is stated that $1\,\text{GeV}/c^2 \approx 1.783 \times 10^{-27}\,\text{kg}$.

Hence, $1\,\text{kg} \approx \dfrac{1}{1.783 \times 10^{-27}}\,\text{GeV}/c^2$

i.e. $1\,\text{kg} \approx 5.61 \times 10^{26}\,\text{GeV}/c^2$

The rest mass of the π^0 is $2.41 \times 10^{-28}\,\text{kg}$

$\approx 2.41 \times 10^{-28}\,\text{kg} \times (5.61 \times 10^{26}\,\text{kg}^{-1}\,\text{GeV}/c^2)$

$\approx 0.14\,\text{GeV}/c^2$

SAQ 4 (a) (i) 540 GeV, (ii) $8.6 \times 10^{-8}\,\text{J}$.

(i) The total kinetic energy of the two particles is $270\,\text{GeV} + 270\,\text{GeV} = 540\,\text{GeV}$.

(ii) Because $1\,\text{GeV} = 10^9\,\text{eV} \times (1.60 \times 10^{-19}\,\text{J eV}^{-1})$
$= 1.60 \times 10^{-10}\,\text{J}$,

it follows that

$540\,\text{GeV} \approx 540\,\text{GeV} \times (1.60 \times 10^{-10}\,\text{J GeV}^{-1})$
$\approx 8.6 \times 10^{-8}\,\text{J}$

(b) Zero. Because the particles collide head-on with the same kinetic energy, their momenta are of the *same* magnitude but of the *opposite* sign. Hence, the total momentum of the particles is zero.

SAQ 5 (c). Statement (c) is false because the μ^+ and the μ^- are both currently believed to be fundamental.

Statement (a) is correct because the μ^+ is the antiparticle of the μ^-. (Remember a particle has the same rest mass as the corresponding antiparticle.) Statement (b) is correct because the μ^+ and the proton both have charge $+e$. Statement (d) is correct because both the μ^- and the μ^+ have charge.

SAQ 6 (a) Yes, the first three lines apply equally well to antineutrinos, which also have zero (or nearly zero) rest mass and which interact only weakly and gravitationally with other matter (Table 3).

(b) The line is scientifically incorrect because neutrinos do interact, weakly and gravitationally, with other matter. A scientifically acceptable version of the line is 'and scarcely interact at all'.

(c) Photons pass through clear glass with only a small amount of scattering, which is why the glass is transparent. The Earth is, in this sense, almost transparent to neutrinos.

SAQ 7 Only reaction (c) can occur because only in this reaction are charge Q, baryon number B and strangeness S conserved:

(c) $K^- + p \rightarrow \bar{K}^0 + n$

Q	$-1 + 1 = \quad 0 + 0$	Q conserved
B	$0 + 1 = \quad 0 + 1$	B conserved
S	$-1 + 0 = -1 + 0$	S conserved

Reaction (a) cannot occur:

(a) $\pi^- + p \nrightarrow n + p$

Q	$-1 + 1 \neq 0 + 1$	Q not conserved
B	$0 + 1 \neq 1 + 1$	B not conserved
S	$0 + 0 = 0 + 0$	S conserved

nor can reaction (b) occur:

(b) $\Sigma^- + p \nrightarrow K^0 + n$

Q	$-1 + 1 = \quad 0 \; + 0$	Q conserved
B	$1 + 1 \neq \quad 0 \; + 1$	B not conserved
S	$-1 + 0 \neq \quad 1 \; + 0$	S not conserved

SAQ 8 The charge of particle X is approximately -1.602×10^{-19} C, X is a baryon and its strangeness is -3.

The question can be answered by writing down the values of the charge Q, baryon number B and strangeness S of the hadrons involved in the reaction, letting the values for each of these intrinsic conserved properties for X be Q_x, B_x and S_x:

$$K^- + p \rightarrow K^0 + K^+ + X$$

Q	$-1 + 1 \quad 0 + 1 \quad + Q_x$	
B	$0 + 1 \quad 0 + 0 \quad + B_x$	
S	$-1 + 0 \quad 1 + 1 \quad + S_x$	

Because the interaction is known to be strong, it follows that charge, baryon number and strangeness must each be conserved. Hence, $Q_x = -1$, $B_x = 1$ and $S_x = -3$.

The statement $Q_x = -1$ means that the charge of X is minus one times the charge of the proton, i.e. $Q_x \approx -1.602 \times 10^{-19}$ C; because $B_x = 1$, X must be a baryon. This baryon was called Ω^-.

SAQ 9 Leptons (c) are currently believed to be fundamental. Mesons and baryons are types of hadrons, and it is known that hadrons have constituents, so they are *not* fundamental particles.

Because mesons and baryons, (a) and (b), are types of hadron they are by definition subject to strong interactions, whereas leptons are *not* subject to these interactions.

SAQ 10 Statements (a) and (c) are correct: quarks and antiquarks are currently believed to be fundamental (i.e. to have no constituents) and they exist in hadrons (Figure 25).

Statement (b) is false because leptons are currently believed to be fundamental particles (Section 3). Statement (d) is false because quarks and antiquarks are subject not only to strong interactions, they are also subject to gravitational interactions (in common with all other particles and antiparticles), to electromagnetic interactions (because they have charge) and to weak interactions. Statement (e) is false: no isolated quark or

isolated antiquark has ever been observed.

SAQ 11 (a) $Q = 0$, $B = 1$, $S = -2$

	u	s	s	
Q	$\frac{2}{3}$	$-\frac{1}{3}$	$-\frac{1}{3}$	$= 0$
B	$\frac{1}{3}$	$+\frac{1}{3}$	$+\frac{1}{3}$	$= 1$
S	0	-1	-1	$= -2$

(b) $Q = 1$, $B = 0$, $S = 0$

	u	$\bar{d}$	
Q	$\frac{2}{3}$	$+\frac{1}{3}$	$= 1$
B	$\frac{1}{3}$	$-\frac{1}{3}$	$= 0$
S	0	$+ 0$	$= 0$

SAQ 12 (a): the J/ψ has constituents. It is a hadron (J/ψ = c$\bar{c}$). Each of the other particles listed is a quark or a lepton (or one of their antiparticles) and is currently believed to be fundamental, i.e. to have no constituents: (b) is a lepton, (c) is an antilepton, (d) is a quark and (e) is an antiquark.

SAQ 13 (a) $Q = 1$, $B = 0$, $S = 1$, $C = 1$, $T = 0$, $B = 0$

	c	$\bar{s}$	
Q	$\frac{2}{3}$	$+\frac{1}{3}$	$= 1$
B	$\frac{1}{3}$	$-\frac{1}{3}$	$= 0$
S	0	$+1$	$= 1$
C	1	$+0$	$= 1$
T	0	$+0$	$= 0$
B	0	$+0$	$= 0$

This hadron has been observed—it is called the D_s^+ and it has a rest mass of approximately 1.971 GeV/c^2.

(b) $Q = 0$, $B = 0$, $S = 0$, $C = 0$, $T = 1$, $B = 0$

	t	$\bar{u}$	
Q	$\frac{2}{3}$	$-\frac{2}{3}$	$= 0$
B	$\frac{1}{3}$	$-\frac{1}{3}$	$= 0$
S	0	$+0$	$= 0$
C	0	$+0$	$= 0$
T	1	$+0$	$= 1$
B	0	$+0$	$= 0$

At the time of going to print (1988), this meson has not been observed.

SAQ 14 Statement (c) is correct: the interactions of the quarks in the constituent protons and neutrons are mediated by gluons (Figure 42).

Statement (a) is false: the photon is currently believed to be fundamental, in common with all the other gauge bosons. Statement (b) is false: from the decay of the W^+, it cannot be concluded that the products are the particle's constituents. Rather, it can be concluded only that the energy of the W^+ can be converted into the kinetic energy and the energy equivalent to the rest masses of the stated products.

INDEX FOR UNIT 32

ACKNOWLEDGEMENTS

Grateful acknowledgement is made to the following sources for permission to use material in this Unit:

J. Updike, 'Cosmic Gall', Copyright © 1960 by John Updike. Reprinted from *Telephone poles and other poems by John Updike* by permission of Alfred A Knopf, Inc. This poem first appeared in *The New Yorker*. UK and Commonwealth rights by permission of Andre Deutsche, London.

Figures 1 and 43 Airtours Publicity Ltd., Altrincham; *Figures 7 and 30* Stanford University: Stanford Linear Accelerator Center; *Figures 8, 15 and 41* Photo CERN; *Figure 13* CERN Courier, Vol. 23, No. 9, November 1983, CERN/DOC; *Figure 16* University of Bristol Cosmic Ray Group; *Figures 18 and 24* California Institute of Technology Archives; *Figure 29* Brookhaven National Laboratory; *Figures 31, 33 and 34* Oxford Nuclear Physics Laboratory/Science Photo Library; *Figure 32 The Times,* 18 November, 1974; *Figure 38* Reportagebild, Stockholm; *Figures 39 and 40* C. Rubbia (1985) 'Experimental observation of the intermediate vector bosons W$^+$, W$^-$ and Z, *Review of Modern Physics,* Vol. 57, No. 3, Part 1, © American Physical Society.